TEXTS IN OPERATIONAL RESEARCH

...erational Research se... ...new generation ...inated tex... ...l relevance of t... ...y's stud... ...ccessibility, the texts ...a non-ma... ...ientation in favour of ...s and busines... ...nce. These texts provide ...grounding in Operational Research they need to ...actitioners, users and innovators of tomorrow.

TEXTS IN OPERATIONAL RESEARCH

Simulation

Roger J. Brooks

Stewart Robinson

Inventory Control

Colin Lewis

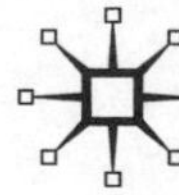

First published 2001 by
PALGRAVE
Houndmills, Basingstoke, Hampshire RG21 6XS and
175 Fifth Avenue, New York, N.Y. 10010
Companies and representatives throughout the world

PALGRAVE is the new global academic imprint of
St. Martin's Press LLC Scholarly and Reference Division and
Palgrave Publishers Ltd (formerly Macmillan Press Ltd).

ISBN 0–333–79429–X (hardback)
ISBN 0–79430–3 (paperback)

This book is printed on paper suitable for recycling and made from fully managed and sustained forest sources.

A catalogue record for this book is available from the British Library.

Formatted by
The Ascenders Partnership, Basingstoke

10 9 8 7 6 5 4 3 2 1
10 09 08 07 06 05 04 03 02 01

Printed and bound in Great Britain by
Creative Print and Design (Wales), Ebbw Vale

Contents

Simulation

Inventory Control

List of Figures

Simulation

Inventory Control

List of Tables

Simulation

Inventory Control

Simulation

Roger J. Brooks
Stewart Robinson

Acknowledgements

Thanks to Simon Taylor (Brunel University) for his help with explaining simulation on more than one computer and to Nuno Melão and Mike Pidd (Lancaster University) for their helpful comments on the manuscript.

1 Introduction

1.1 Importance of models

HOW would you like to have a machine that would predict the future? Of course, such a machine would be very valuable. Most of the decisions we take in our daily lives are greatly influenced by what we expect to happen in the future, not least that we expect the sun to rise again tomorrow! For instance, plans and timetables are provided to aid the taking of decisions by making the future more predictable, since they say at what times particular things are going to happen, whether it be transport, television programmes or lectures. Problems can result if the future does not match the timetable, however!

Often, the way we predict what is going to happen in the future is to observe what has happened in the past and extract certain patterns and relationships that we assume will continue to apply. These patterns and relationships can be called a model because they are a representation (in abstract form) of some part of the real world. For as far back as humans have existed they have probably used models; for example, by observing the behaviour of animals and plants at different times of the year and in different weather to develop good strategies for hunting and farming. The ability to predict the movements of the sun, moon and stars also appear to have been very important to our ancestors, judging by some of the impressive stone monuments that they built apparently for this purpose.

As our knowledge has increased of the world around us, our ability to model has become more sophisticated. The development of mathematics and, more recently, the development of computers have provided powerful tools for model building. Models of various forms are widely used in nearly all areas of science and, indeed, a scientific hypothesis can be regarded as a model. Some well-known scientific models are Newton's laws of motion and the model of the atom, originally proposed by Bohr, as a nucleus with electrons in distinct orbits. A model can then be used to predict what will happen in particular conditions in the future and sometimes to estimate the consequences of taking different actions. The results of chaos theory, however, show that in some circumstances there are fundamental limits to the predictive accuracy that models can achieve.

Companies also want to predict the future, and, particularly, they want to know what the effects will be of all the possible decisions that they might take so that they can choose the best thing to do. Often they have to make decisions about very complicated situations with many uncertainties. Even if precise predictions are not possible, knowledge of the possible outcomes that may occur is extremely valuable as it allows an assessment of the risks involved. Again, models can be powerful tools to do this.

1.2 Simulation and other models

A model can be defined, in general, as a simplified representation of something. The model is always simpler in some way than the original object or system being represented; otherwise it would just be a copy. Different types of model use different forms of representation, which can be scale, schematic, analogue or mathematical (Shannon, 1975).

Scale models are physical models which have the same shape as the original but usually scaled up or scaled down (for example, model aeroplanes or model buildings). Schematic models, such as a map, use diagrams and symbols to show aspects of the original. Where it is behaviour that is of interest, analogue models can sometimes be used. Then, the model and the original are of quite different form but have characteristics that can be related to each other. For example, flows of electrical current can be used to represent flows of a fluid or even flows of material around a production line. However, most models of behaviour are mathematical, using variables, relationships and equations.

Operational Research is largely based on mathematical models including queueing models, linear programs, forecasting models, network models and simulation. However, the way a simulation model works is different to many other types of mathematical model. The approach used in simulation is to represent what is happening at a local scale without imposing a particular overall structure that the model must fit into. The model consists of many objects, each with their own behaviour, that interact with each other. The overall behaviour of the system results from these interactions. For example, simulation models of the weather divide the atmosphere into many small cells (often cubes). Each cell has particular physical attributes such as temperature, wind speed and humidity. Equations are then used to determine how these attributes will change over time depending on the values in the neighbouring cells. As a result of these many interactions between cells the model as a whole will then predict how the weather will change. This may include the development and movement of a low pressure region even though such a region is not specifically included in the model but just arises because of the dynamics of the atmosphere.

Simulation, then, consists of building a virtual world out of small components. A very important consequence is that simulation is an experimental approach. The user is able to change parts of the model and to observe the resulting behaviour. If the user wishes to improve the operations of the system represented by the model, the user will do this by altering the components in the model, essentially by trial and error. This is often called a 'what if' approach since the model helps to answer 'what if' type questions. For example, a model of a production line might be used to answer questions such as 'what if we bought a new machine for one of the processes?'.

The simulation approach is quite different to that of linear programming (Wisniewski, 2001 in this series) for example. With linear programming, the problem being investigated must fit into a particular format, namely a linear objective function with linear constraints. The model itself has a rigid structure that the problem has to conform to. The advantage of this is that a linear program can be solved analytically to produce an optimal solution whereas simulation cannot. The main disadvantage is that linear programming is restricted to only certain types of problems, whereas it is the great flexibility of simulation that makes it one of the most widely used Operational Research techniques as well as being used extensively in many areas of science.

One form of simulation that you will be familiar with is the computer game. This creates a virtual world of some sort and sets a problem to solve, whether it is to kill lots of monsters, to use a series of clues to solve a mystery or to score more goals than the opposing football team. Notice that any game will only allow certain types of behaviour and will not be totally realistic in the movements represented. This is part of the simplification present in any simulation – no model can include everything but what should be included are the important aspects of the system for the particular problem.

Computer games also usually come with impressive graphics. With simulation in a business context, the main emphasis should be on the analysis and understanding of the behaviour of the model. Many simulation software packages do include facilities for sophisticated animation, however, and a good visual display can be very useful for communication purposes and for observing the model as it runs. Nevertheless, the fact that a model looks like the real system is not a substitute for properly testing that it does behave in a similar way to the real system.

Indeed, you may have played games which are either very unrealistic or which have features that do not work properly. This is a frustrating experience. Similarly, with simulation in business, it is very important to test that the model works as intended and that it is a sufficiently good representation of the real world.

Experimenting with a computer game (that is, playing the game) will often enable the player to develop good strategies to solve the problem, as well as finding out that certain strategies do not work. This is similar to the way in which simulation is used in general. However, careful planning of the experiments to be carried out and sound analysis of the results can help in finding a good solution more quickly.

1.3 Types of simulation model

Simulation models can be categorized depending on how time is represented and whether they include any randomness. Simulation models that do not include time at all are called static, for example, the evaluation of difficult integrals by choosing sample values. However, most simulation models do include time because it is the way that the system changes over time that is of interest. Such models are called dynamic.

In dynamic models, the variations over time can be simulated in two different ways. In a discrete model, behaviour only changes at an instant of time (an event), with constant behaviour between the events. Continuous models, on the other hand, represent continual changes, often using differential equations, so that the behaviour in the model is always altering. In business systems it is usually unnecessary to model changes continuously and so a discrete model provides a simpler and more appropriate representation. Often, the important aspects of the system do change in a discrete way. For example, a machine starts working on a part at a particular instant in time.

Random numbers are used in simulation to simulate variable, unpredictable behaviour such as the time at which the next customer will arrive at a bank or the time at which a machine will next break down. Plausible sample values are chosen to model such behaviour. A great advantage of simulation is its ability to model variable behaviour in this way. Models that include random numbers are called stochastic whereas those that do not are called deterministic. Most Operational Research simulation models are dynamic, discrete and stochastic and so this book concentrates on this type of simulation model.

1.4 Applications of simulation

Simulation is used to help to tackle a wide variety of types of business problems including:

- Planning. Simulating a proposed new business operation helps in deciding what to include as well as how it should be laid out. Examples include building a new factory or production process, and designing new distribution routes or transportation systems.
- Decision-making. All businesses have to decide between alternatives. For example, a manufacturing company may be considering whether to buy a new machine (and which machine to buy) or a hospital may be deciding how many doctors and nurses are needed in the casualty department. Simulation can be used to predict the outcome of each choice and can sometimes lead to solutions that had not previously been thought of. This is probably the most important use of simulation in business.
- Prediction. Simulation is sometimes carried out just to predict what is going to happen in situations in which the user cannot exert any influence. This includes certain economic models of the market in which the company operates. The results of the simulation can then be fed into the decision-making process of the company.

- Training. By creating a virtual world, simulation provides a safe environment in which training can take place. Examples include flight simulators to train pilots, air traffic control simulators to train the controllers, and business games for managers.
- Communication. Many simulation models have a good visual display showing what the model is doing. This can help the problem-solving process by allowing many people to have an input into the building of the model by comparing observations of the model with their knowledge of how the real system works. This tends to be an additional benefit of simulation so that, for example, as well as helping a decision to be made, the model also helps all those involved to understand the basis on which it is being taken.

Although there are many different applications of simulation, one objective of building and using a simulation model should always be to improve the understanding of the way the system works. Even the process of building the model encourages the user to think in a systematic way about the processes taking place in the real world. In simulation, the behaviour of the model can be observed as the simulation runs and it is possible to look inside the model to analyse the reasons for the results which can lead to important insights into the relationships existing in the real world. Lessons learned in this way can then be applied in the future, even when conditions change.

1.5 Why simulate?

Simulation consists of building a representation of the real world and experimenting with it and therefore one alternative to simulation is actually to experiment with the real world itself. However, it is usually highly undesirable to carry out the experiments on the real world for the following reasons (Robinson, 1994; Pidd, 1998):

- Cost. It is likely to be much cheaper to build a model than to experiment with the real system. When comparing alternative decisions, for example, each one would have to be implemented in the real world. If considering whether to purchase a new machine, it would have to be bought and used just to test whether it was worth buying!

- Time. The speed of a simulation model depends on its size and complexity, how it is built and the hardware it runs on, but most models run much faster than real time. For instance, the model may only have to run for a few minutes to simulate the future behaviour of the system over many years. This enables results to be used now that would take years to obtain from the real world. The model gives control over time within the virtual world and, in fact, it can be beneficial in some circumstances for the model to run slower than real time (for instance, when modelling computer systems). This allows interactions in the system to be observed in the model that would be very difficult to observe in the real world because they happen so fast (like a slow motion replay).
- Repeatability. Experiments on a simulation model can be repeated exactly, just by re-running the model under the same conditions. This allows further analysis to be carried out to investigate the reasons for a particular result. Repeating an experiment in the real world will not give identical results because conditions are always changing.
- Safety. Simulation can be used to model dangerous situations such as the evacuation procedures for an approaching hurricane, or the dispersion of poisonous gases after a chemical leak. It is clearly not a good idea to create these situations in the real world just to see what happens. Simulation also provides a safe environment for training by allowing mistakes to be made without serious consequences. Even in more general applications, such as factory planning, it is better to explore the safety implications of a new layout using a model than by trial and error in the real world.
- Real system does not exist. In this case experimenting with the real world is not an option! Simulation may be used to investigate systems that are not feasible with current technology.

1.6 Summary

Simulation is a powerful tool that can help in many business problems. As with any tool it is only beneficial if it is used properly whereas inappropriate use can be damaging to the business. The aim of this book is to provide the basis for the successful application of simulation. The foundation for this is to understand what is happening in a simulation model and this is explained in Chapter 2. Most simulation models nowadays are built using a software package and Chapter 3 describes the main features that such packages provide. A simulation project involves many activities from understanding the problem to be tackled, to choosing, building, testing and experimenting with the model, leading to implementation of a solution. Chapter 4 sets out how a simulation project should be approached. Simulation is still a developing discipline and Chapter 5 gives an introduction to further topics in simulation modelling and the main areas of current research. Finally, Chapter 6 summarizes the main benefits of simulation and the circumstances in which it should be applied.

References and further reading

Pidd, M. (1998) *Computer Simulation in Management Science*, 4th edn. Chichester, UK: Wiley.

Robinson, S. (1994) *Successful Simulation: A Practical Approach to Simulation Projects*. Maidenhead, UK: McGraw-Hill.

Shannon, R.E. (1975) *Systems Simulation: The Art and Science*. Englewood Cliffs, NJ: Prentice-Hall.

Wisniewski, M. (2001) *Linear Programming*. Basingstoke: Palgrave.

2 How a Simulation Model Works

2.1 Introduction

The purpose of this chapter is to explain the principles and mechanics underlying a simulation model. Usually, a simulation model is built using a specialist simulation software package (Chapter 3). This chapter shows what is happening inside such a package which is a vital foundation for undertaking a simulation project. For instance, steps in a simulation project include deciding what to include in the model, building the model, experimenting with it and interpreting the results (Chapter 4). These cannot be done properly unless the modeller understands what the model is doing and the assumptions implicitly contained in the model. Without this understanding it is easy for the results of a simulation project to be useless, or, worse, misleading.

Sometimes it is necessary to build a simulation model in a programming language, for instance, when the model is too complex for a standard software package (Section 3.2). The material in this chapter also provides a basis for constructing your own simulation models from scratch.

The chapter starts by considering what elements make up a simulation model through the simple example of a cash machine at a bank. The elements are then explained in turn in more detail. A hand simulation shows how the elements work together using an extended simulation of the bank.

2.2 Elements of a simulation model

Suppose we want to simulate a simple queueing system such as customers arriving and using an Automatic Teller Machine (ATM) at a bank (for example, to withdraw cash or check their account balance). What are the tasks that the model has to perform?

In order to answer this, the first thing is to establish what the model is going to be used for, because the project objectives should drive all parts of the project. Suppose that in this case a machine is being installed for the first time and the aim is to predict how long the customers are likely to have to queue at peak times.

The model only has to represent the behaviour that relates in some way to the project objectives – in this case, whatever affects customers' queueing times at the ATM. In general, the issue of what to include and what to exclude from the model can be quite difficult and is explored further in Section 4.3. However, here the queueing times will depend on the times when the customers arrive at the ATM and the time each customer spends using the ATM. Therefore, the model needs to simulate customers arriving, queueing to use the machine, using the machine and then leaving.

In order to achieve this the model has to contain certain objects found in the real system and to give them particular behaviour. In fact, the origins of 'object-oriented' programming can be found in developments in simulation software (Dahl and Nygaard, 1966). In this case, the objects required are the customers and the ATM. The objects used in a simulation model are called entities.

In discrete event simulation, the behaviour of these entities consists of a sequence of events. The events happen at an instant in time, with the detailed behaviour between events not being represented. Instead, the model just records a description of what the entity is doing (which may include doing nothing) and then only needs to know the time or circumstances at which this will change. The description of the behaviour of an entity at a particular time is called the state of the entity. States of the customer include waiting for the machine and using the machine.

To build a particular model, the modeller has to specify what the entities, states and events are and also certain rules that determine when each event happens and the effect of each event. In the ATM model, events are the arrival of a customer, a customer starting to use the machine and a customer finishing using the machine. The rules include the circumstances in which a customer starts to use the machine. This will happen when there is a customer waiting and the machine is free.

As is normally the case with simulation, there are aspects of the real system here that are uncertain. It is not possible to know at precisely what time the customers will arrive in the future or how long each customer will spend using the machine. The approach taken by simulation in such circumstances is to generate typical values. These are usually obtained by choosing values at random from a probability distribution that specifies the overall behaviour of the uncertain events. The model therefore needs to have some way of making random selections and simulation models do this by producing random numbers using a random number generator. This is a vital part of most simulation models in Operational Research.

Once the entities, events and event rules have been specified, the model then has to have some way of organizing the behaviour of the entities so that everything happens in the correct order when the model is run. The model may contain many entities interacting with each other and so this can be a complex task. The part of the model that does this is called the simulation executive.

In order to manage the process correctly during a model run, the simulation executive keeps a record of the current time in the simulation using a simulation clock, and a record of the current state in the simulated system. The simulation executive also keeps an event list, which is a diary recording the next scheduled events that will happen to each entity. This tells the executive which event to perform next and the time at which it will occur. When an event is carried out, the event rules specify the changes to be made to the system and also provide the information to update the event list.

The simulation model also needs some way to collect statistics as the model runs in order to provide useful results. The user should be able to specify the information to be recorded. Here, for example, this could consist of the time spent queueing by each customer or the average queueing time of the customers. The simulation model elements are shown in Figure 2.1.

In summary, then, a simulation model consists of:

- Simulation executive
- Simulation clock
- Random number generator
- Entities
- Events and states
- Event rules
- Record of the current state of the entities
- Event list
- Collection and recording of output statistics.

Some of these simulation elements are the architecture that forms the simulation environment for any model that the modeller inputs. These are the simulation executive which keeps the current state, simulation clock and event list during the run, the random number generator and the general output facilities. For a particular

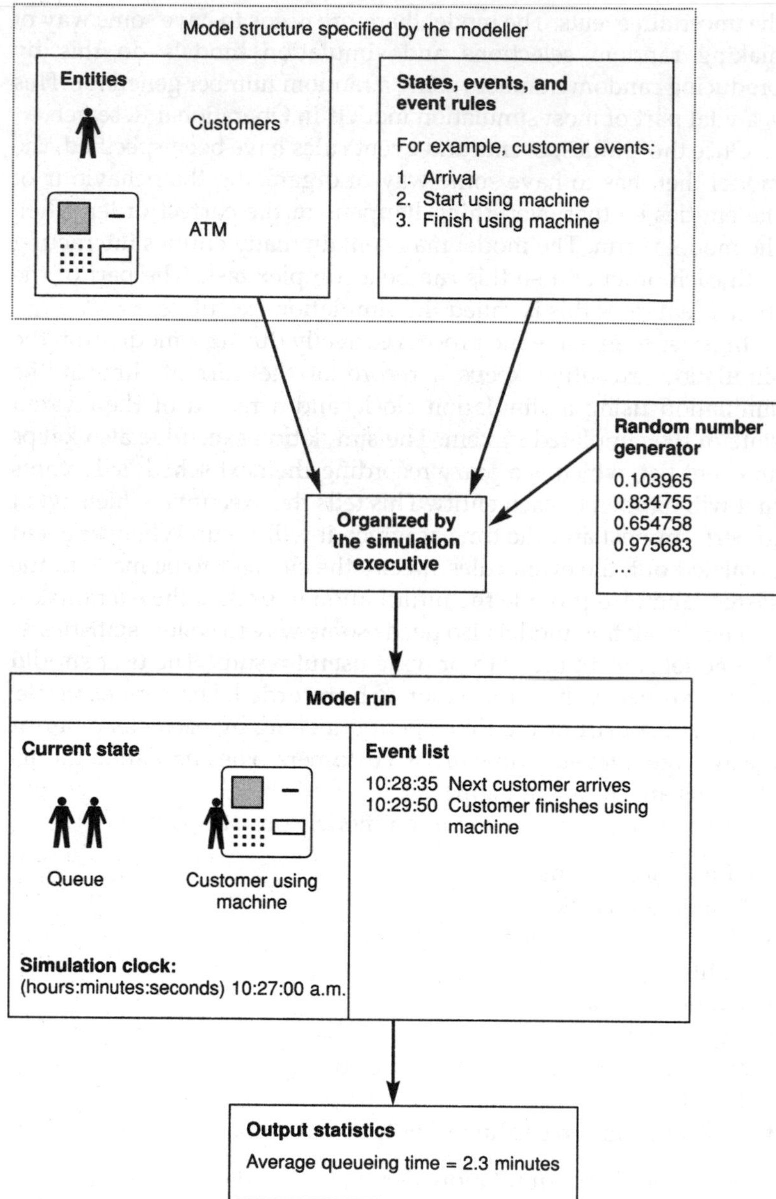

Figure 2.1 Simulation model elements for the ATM simulation

model, the modeller then provides the details of the entities, states, events and event rules as well as procedures for recording specific output values. Modern simulation software may also provide other facilities such as predefined entities (templates that reduce the amount of information the user has to provide), default statistics and many visual display features (Section 3.2).

When building a model, it is always useful to consider what is being excluded. These are the simplifications from the real world to the model and so are implicit assumptions made in the modelling process. Here, for example, what potential customers do before they arrive is not modelled (customer 1 might have breakfast, drive to the shops, walk round the shops, then go to the ATM and so on). The model also excludes details of what is happening during the periods of constant state between the events. Here, this includes the detail of the customers operating the machine – whether they display their balance, withdraw cash, request a statement, and so on. All that is modelled is the time they spend using the machine. Certain rare events such as the machine being out of service due to a fault or lack of cash are also excluded. This is because it is only the level of service under normal operating conditions that is being considered here.

Sections 2.3–2.6 now explain the elements of a simulation model in more detail. Section 2.3 explains the information required to specify the entities, states and events when building a simulation model. The use of random numbers to simulate variability is considered in Section 2.4 and then Section 2.5 shows how the executive coordinates the simulation. Section 2.6 discusses useful statistics to collect. The best way to understand how a simulation model works is to do an example by hand and Section 2.7 explains each step for an extended bank simulation.

Sections 2.3–2.7 use the 'three-phase' simulation approach. Although there are several simulation approaches, they are all based on the principles described above and only differ in the precise way the events are organized. The three-phase approach is followed here because we think it is the easiest to understand and the most flexible approach. The other approaches are briefly described in Section 2.8.

2.3 Entities, events and states

As we have already seen, a discrete event simulation model is made up of a number of entities whose changes in behaviour are represented using instantaneous events. Between the events the entities are in a constant state in which their behaviour does not change. As a result, a run of a simulation model consists of periods of constant state separated by the events, as shown in Figure 2.2. A simulation model is therefore constructed by deciding what entities, states and events need to be modelled.

Most situations can be described approximately in this way. For example, perhaps your activities this afternoon could be represented by the states and events: state 1 = eating lunch, event 1 = end of lunch, state 2 = walk to lecture theatre, event 2 = arrive at lecture theatre, state 3 = wait for lecture to start, event 3 = start of lecture, state 4 = in lecture, event 4 = end of lecture, and so on.

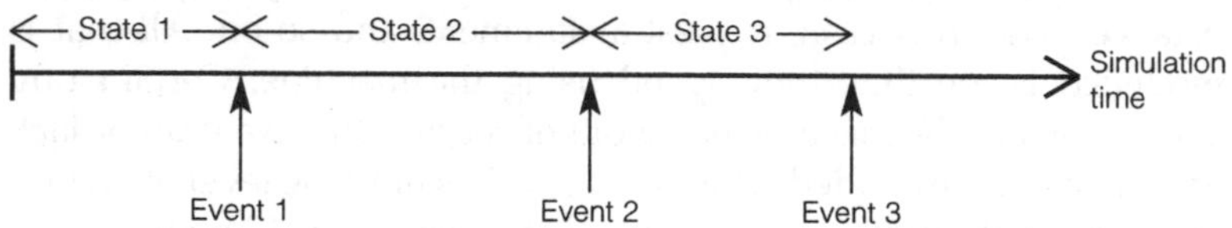

Figure 2.2 General behaviour of a run of a discrete event simulation model

2.3.1 Entities

Entities are the objects of interest in the system that are included in the model. Typical entities are customers, servers (whether humans or machines), manufacturing machines, parts, labour and vehicles. The main entities that the model should include are often clear, although the general question of what to include in the model (such as what states and events) is an important issue that is discussed in Section 4.3.

There are two main ways of modelling the entities in a system. One is to record the state of each individual item. In other words, each item is monitored throughout the system. For example, information would be kept about where each different customer is. For instance, customer number 22 might be third in the queue for the ATM. The second way is just to keep a record of how many of a particular entity are in a certain state. So, the model might just record that there are five customers in the queue.

If each individual item is monitored then the simulation has a lot of information to update when an event occurs. For example, once the person using the machine has finished, the first person in the queue for the machine can then start using the machine. The simulation model would delete this particular customer from the queue and record that this customer was now using the machine. In addition, it would also have to update the position of each of the other customers in the queue. The advantage of this approach, however, is that information can be collected about each customer that can be useful in analysing the results of the simulation.

In contrast, if only the number of customers at each stage in the process is recorded, the simulation just has to note that one person is using the machine and has to reduce the number queueing by one. Instead of keeping detailed records, the behaviour of the customers is reduced to just a number of variables, one for each possible state. In the simulation literature, the term entity is sometimes used just for objects modelled in the first of these two ways, with objects modelled in the second way called resources (Pidd, 1998), although we will not make this distinction.

Various additional pieces of information, called attributes, may be recorded to describe the entities. This information is usually used for entities modelled individually to distinguish between different types of a particular entity by describing characteristics such as the nature of the transaction of a customer or the length, colour or other specification of a part. This information may just make the simulation easier to understand or it may be important for the logic of the simulation if, for example, different types of entity take a different route through some of the system. It can often be simpler to distinguish between different types of entity using attributes than to use a separate entity for each type. Attributes can also be used for dynamic information that changes as an item passes through the system, such as whether a part needs reworking. Again, this can form part of the simulation logic. Attributes can also record data about the experience of the particular item in the model, such as queueing time, that can then be used to calculate output statistics.

2.3.2 Events and states

The easiest way to identify the events and states is usually to take each entity in turn and consider the path through the system that the entity goes along. The alternate states and instantaneous events for the customer in the ATM example are shown in Table 2.1. All the possible states and events are shown even though some of them may not actually take place for some customers. If a customer arrives at the machine and it is free, the customer will not have to wait, as there is no queue, but can start using the machine straight away. The general pattern shown by Table 2.1 can still be considered to apply, however – it is just that the time spent in state 2 will be zero. Since it is easier to work with a single general specification of events and states, a simulation model would deal with such a customer in this way. It would first perform event 1 to change the customer to state *wait for machine* and then it would immediately perform event 2 so that the customer starts using the machine.

Table 2.1 States and events of ATM customers

State 1	Going to machine
Event 1	Arrive at machine
State 2	Wait for machine
Event 2	Start using machine
State 3	Using machine
Event 3	Finish using machine
State 4	Elsewhere

The behaviour of customers can be represented pictorially in an activity cycle diagram (Hills, 1971; Pidd, 1998). Such a diagram shows the states and distinguishes between active states drawn as rectangles and passive (or dead) states drawn as circles. In an active state, the time spent in that state is known when the state commences, whereas in a passive state this is not known. Active states are also called 'activities' as the entity is usually carrying out some task. The duration of the task is determined in the simulation when the task starts. Passive states, on the other hand, are the occasions when the entity has to wait or queue until something becomes available. The arrows between the states represent events. Figure 2.3 shows the activity cycle diagram for the ATM customers.

In a system like this that starts with the entity arriving, the initial state of *going to machine* is an active state. This is because as soon as one customer arrives, the inter-arrival time of the next customer is determined by the simulation and so the time until this customer

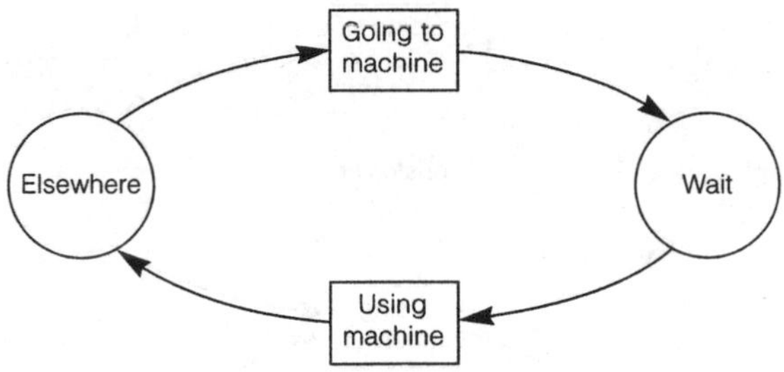

Figure 2.3 Activity cycle diagram for ATM customers

arrives at the machine is known. The diagram is conventionally shown as a cycle by connecting the first and last states indicating that there is a continual flow of customers round the system, although this is not essential.

Notice that the activity cycle diagram consists of alternate passive and active states. The occurrence of consecutive passive or active states may indicate that they can be combined, thus simplifying the model. For example, *using the machine* could be split into two (or more) states such as putting in the card and operating the machine. Since the second event automatically follows the first, they can be combined into a single state with just a single duration being required rather than choosing two separate durations. In more complicated systems, consecutive active or passive states can sometimes occur in which case dummy states are usually inserted to maintain the alternating active and passive states (Pidd, 1998).

In a similar way, an activity cycle diagram can be drawn for the machine (Figure 2.4) and the two diagrams can be combined into an overall diagram for the model (Figure 2.5).

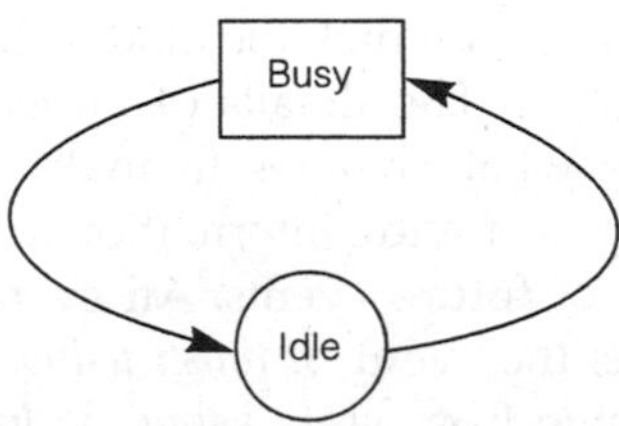

Figure 2.4 Activity cycle diagram for the ATM

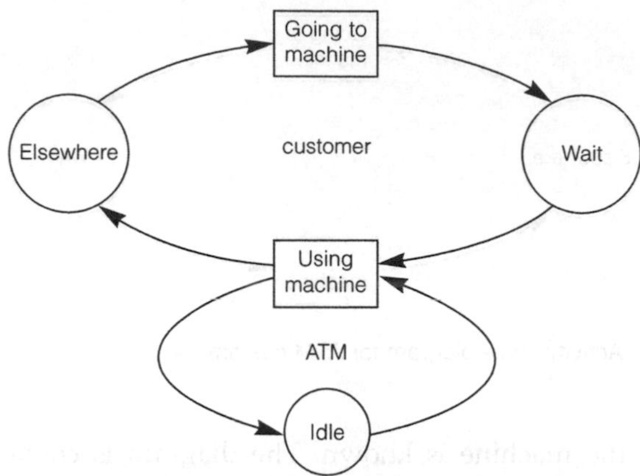

Figure 2.5 Activity cycle diagram for the complete ATM model

An activity cycle diagram is an aid to model building rather than a necessity. It can help in the process of deciding what to include in the model, both in terms of the entities to include and the level of detail at which changes in behaviour need to be represented (Section 4.3). It can also help in the process of constructing the model by providing a model structure. However, for complex models the activity cycle diagram can also become complicated, particularly where there are different paths that the entity could take, depending on interactions with other entities. Alternatives to activity cycle diagrams include logic flowcharts, event graphs (Schruben, 1983) or simply a table of behaviour as in Table 2.1. Some documentation of the logic behind the model is very important in providing a reference point throughout the modelling project of how the model should operate.

2.3.3 Event details and rules

The events are the points at which the model changes the behaviour of the simulated system. The details of an event need to tell the simulation executive what changes to make to the states of the entities and also need to provide information to update the event list that keeps the diary of future events. An event may affect several entities. For example, the event of *finish using machine* both causes the customer to change from state *using machine* to state *elsewhere* and causes the machine to change from state *busy* to state *idle*.

In the three-phase approach, there are two different types of events, bound and conditional (sometimes just called B and C events). A bound event is one that can be scheduled in advance as a consequence of a previous event – once the previous event occurs it is bound to happen. For example, *finish using machine* is a bound event. When the customer starts using the machine, the duration of use will be determined by the simulation, and so the event *finish using machine* can be scheduled that amount of time later. Bound events are scheduled by adding them to the event list (the diary of future events). The precise way in which the executive uses the event list is explained in Section 2.5.

A conditional event occurs only when certain conditions are satisfied and cannot be scheduled in advance. Instead, the occurrence of another event may cause the conditions to be met. This will trigger the conditional event to happen immediately, without the time changing on the simulation clock. The event *start using machine* is a conditional event with the condition that it only occurs when the machine is idle and there is a customer waiting. There are two circumstances that will cause this event to happen. The first is that there are no customers waiting and the machine is idle, and then the event *arrival* occurs so that a customer arrives and is now waiting. The second is that there is a customer waiting and the machine is being used, and then the event *finish using machine* occurs so that the machine becomes idle.

In activity cycle diagram terms an active state (such as *using machine*) usually starts with a conditional event (*start using machine*) and ends with a bound event (*finish using machine*). Entities tend to have to wait for certain conditions to apply before being able to undertake the next activity, and so the start of an activity is a conditional event changing the entity from a passive to an active state. The time spent in an active state is known when the state starts and so the event to end the activity can be scheduled as a bound event. Therefore one aspect of the event details for most conditional events is to specify the bound events to be added to the event list.

In this example, there is also one bound event that adds an event to the event list, which is the *arrival* event. This is because there is a constant stream of arrivals and so, as soon as one customer arrives, the arrival of the next customer can be scheduled immediately by choosing the next inter-arrival time. The inter-arrival time is the duration of the active *going to machine* state in Figure 2.5. The constant stream of arrivals means that a conditional event is not required to start this state as it automatically starts when the previous customer arrives.

Since entities usually experience alternate passive and active states, the sequence of events for an entity normally consists of alternate bound and conditional events. One effect of the bound event at the end of an activity (such as *finish using machine*) is often to make resources available (the machine becomes *idle*). This may in turn trigger a conditional event for another entity that was waiting (the next customer in the queue can start using the machine). However, this process is handled automatically by the simulation executive (Section 2.5) without needing to be specified in the event details.

The details required for each event are therefore its type, the conditions for it to occur (for conditional events), the changes in state to make and the events to add to the event list. Table 2.2 gives the details of the events in the ATM example. Simulation software can also include events to update the visual display to ensure that the animation is smooth.

Table 2.2 Event details for the ATM simulation

Event	***Type***	***Conditions for event to occur***	***Change in state caused by event***	***Future events to schedule***
Arrival	Bound		Add new customer to end of queue with state *wait for machine*	Next *arrival* (by choosing an inter-arrival time)
Start using machine	Conditional	Machine state is *idle* and there is a customer waiting	Change state of customer at front of queue from state *wait for machine* to state *using machine*. Change state of machine from *idle* to *busy*	*Finish using machine* (by choosing the time spent by the customer using the machine)
Finish using machine	Bound		Change state of customer from *using machine* to *elsewhere*. Change state of machine from *busy* to *idle*	

This model has just a single ATM to serve the customers. The addition of more machines would make very little difference to the model specification. Indeed, the activity cycle diagram would not change. All that would be required are slight changes to the *start using machine* event. The first part of the condition for this event would change to 'at least one machine is *idle*'. The event would also have to specify the order in which the machines are chosen by a customer if several machines are free, which could be a random order.

2.4 Random numbers and variability

Random numbers are used in most Operational Research simulation models to simulate variability. Certain aspects of the real system being modelled will change from one occasion to the next in unpredictable ways. These include human behaviour such as the time between successive arrivals or the time to serve a customer. For instance, at a supermarket checkout one customer could take 3 mins 15 secs to serve whereas the next may require only 1 min 30 secs. In automated systems, such as machines in a production line, the time between breakdowns and the time to repair the machines will vary considerably from one breakdown to the next. Even machine processing times may be quite different for each successive part.

The variability in a system usually has a crucial role in determining the behaviour of the system. For example, if customers arrived at the ATM an equal time apart and used the machine for a constant length of time, it would be easy to predict what will happen. In particular, if the time using the machine was less than the inter-arrival time no one would ever have to queue. It is the variability in both these times that means that in reality sometimes a queue will form whereas sometimes the machine will be idle for a period of time. It is therefore essential that such variability is included in the model.

For some aspects of the system, it may be acceptable to use an average value but great care must be taken before doing so. If the variations are small compared to other variations in the system then an average may be appropriate. This can always be tested by adding in the variability and seeing if this affects the results.

In most cases, the overall behaviour of a variable characteristic in the long term can be described using a probability distribution. Perhaps the service times of some process may follow a normal distribution, for example. The model can then simulate the characteristic by choosing a value at random from the distribution. The sampling of values at random from a distribution is done using random numbers.

Simulation software therefore has to have some way of obtaining random numbers. This is done using a computer program called a random number generator. The next section explains how random number generators work and then Section 2.4.2 shows how the resulting random numbers can be used to choose values from different types of probability distributions. Software also often allows different sequences of random numbers to be used for different purposes and the benefits of doing this are explained in Section 2.4.3. Finally, Section 2.4.4 looks at choosing random numbers by hand from a random number table.

2.4.1 Random number generators

A random number generator is a computer program used to produce random numbers. It is a numerical algorithm that generates a sequence of numbers, with the most common algorithms producing numbers between 0 and 1 (for example, 0.1387, 0.6209). Providing an input value called a seed initializes the algorithm. If the same seed is used then the same sequence of numbers will be produced. This is an advantage in simulation because it allows an experiment to be repeated exactly (Section 1.5).

Numbers produced by such a method are not truly random in the sense that they come from a deterministic algorithm. Generators are therefore often called pseudo-random number generators. In fact, philosophically, it is hard to define precisely what is meant by random numbers, but they are usually thought of as values coming from certain types of physical process that we cannot predict, such as the time of decay of a radioactive particle. The selection of numbered balls for a lottery is also intended to be a random process!

However, there are two properties that we would want the random numbers produced by a random number generator to have. Most generators aim to sample evenly across the interval 0 to 1 (that is, from the uniform U[0,1] distribution). Therefore, the first property is that the chance of getting a number from any part of the interval 0 to 1 should be proportional to the width of that part of the interval. So, for example, the chance of the generator producing a number between 0.2 and 0.3 should be 10 per cent.

The second property is that there should be no correlation between successive numbers, or between each number and the second number following, and so on. In other words, the fact that the number just generated is 0.1387 does not affect the likelihood that the next number will be close to 1 or close to 0 – it is still equally likely to come anywhere between 0 and 1. Statistically speaking, the numbers should be independent. A number of tests have been devised to assess how well algorithms perform for these characteristics (for example, Banks *et al.*, 1996). The importance of the characteristics also depends on precisely what the random numbers will be used for. A flawed random number generator can cause the simulation to produce very misleading results.

One limitation that most algorithms have is that the sequence of numbers produced will eventually repeat. Hence it is important that the sequence is longer than the number of random numbers used in the experiments on the model. The computer function implementing the algorithm also needs to have a short execution time if many random numbers are needed, otherwise it may reduce the run speed of the simulation considerably.

Most simulation packages have built-in algorithms for generating random numbers and so the user is forced to rely on the software provider using a good algorithm. The most commonly used generators are based on the linear or multiplicative congruential generator, which is explained in Appendix I. If a simulation is being programmed in a computer language then most languages also come with a random number function provided, although these are often of poor quality. A better approach is to choose and code your own random number generator. A selection of suitable functions for most languages, along with a good discussion, can be found in the Numerical Recipes series (for example, Press *et al.*, 1992).

2.4.2 Using probability distributions

An empirical probability distribution is sometimes obtained by collecting data about the variable characteristic of interest. For example, observations of the service times of 200 customers using an ATM may find the following:

Table 2.3 Example data of time spent by customers using an ATM

Time using the machine (to nearest 30 secs)	*No. of people*
30	20
60	56
90	90
120	34

Values for the simulation can be obtained by sampling directly from this distribution. To do this, we first calculate the proportion of people in each category. These proportions are the desired probabilities of selecting each category. Cumulative proportions can then be calculated easily and random numbers can be related to each category using these proportions as shown in Table 2.4.

Table 2.4 Allocation of random numbers to times

Time using the machine (to nearest 30 secs)	*Proportion of people*	*Cumulative proportion*	*Interval for random number, r*
30	0.10	0.10	$0.00 \le r < 0.10$
60	0.28	0.38	$0.10 \le r < 0.38$
90	0.45	0.83	$0.38 \le r < 0.83$
120	0.17	1.00	$0.83 \le r \le 1.00$

The required probability that the time = 30 is 0.10 and therefore the interval from 0 to 0.10 is assigned to this category. The probability for time = 60 is 0.28 and so the next interval of width 0.28 is assigned to this category, namely 0.10 to 0.38, and so on. The end points of these intervals are the cumulative proportions.

To select a time, the random number generator is used to produce a random number between 0 and 1. The interval in Table 2.4 that the random number falls within then determines the time chosen. Table 2.5 shows the corresponding times for various random numbers.

Standard probability distributions can also be used. A particular distribution may fit the data well or there may be theoretical reasons for believing that the distribution applies. For example, a common assumption is that customers arrive at random with no

Table 2.5 Examples of random numbers and the times that would be chosen

Random number	*Time chosen (to nearest 30 secs)*
0.2508	60
0.9982	120
0.0915	30
0.8516	120
0.3804	90

correlation between arrivals (that is, they do not arrive in groups). If the average arrival rate stays constant, it can be shown that the times between successive arrivals will follow the negative exponential distribution (see Figure 4.8). Section 4.3 sets out the probability distributions that are commonly used in simulation.

As for an empirical distribution, random numbers are also used to sample from a standard probability distribution. For some distributions, including the negative exponential, the cumulative probability function can be used. The cumulative probability takes values from 0 to 1. Values can be chosen from the distribution by obtaining a random number, r, between 0 and 1 and then finding the value from the distribution that has this cumulative probability. This is similar to the approach above for the empirical distribution where the cumulative probabilities were used to find the intervals in Table 2.4.

For the negative exponential distribution the value selected using this method is given by the formula:

$$x = -\mu \ln(1 - r) \tag{2.1}$$

where,

r is the random number between 0 and 1 used for the selection;
μ is the mean of the negative exponential distribution being used;
ln is the natural logarithm function;
x is the resulting value chosen from the negative exponential distribution.

The derivation of the formula is given in Appendix II.

For example, suppose customers arrive at random at a shop at a rate of 20 per hour. Suppose the random numbers chosen for the first two arrivals are 0.2047 and 0.6835. If the shop opens at 9 am, at what time will the customers arrive in the simulation?

A rate of 20 customers per hour is a mean time between arrivals of 3 mins. So, using equation 2.1, the inter-arrival times are given by $x = -3\ln(1 - r)$. The first random number is $r = 0.2047$ and putting this into the equation gives x = 0.69 mins (working to two decimal places). So the customer will arrive at 9 am + 0.69 mins = 9 am and 41 secs. Using $r = 0.6835$, the inter-arrival time of the second customer is 3.45 mins = 3 mins and 27 secs. So, the second customer will arrive 3 mins and 27 secs after the first at 4 mins and 8 secs past 9 am.

Another distribution that is easy to sample from is the uniform distribution over the interval between two numbers a and b, U[a,b] (see Figure 4.11). The random numbers come from the uniform distribution on the interval between 0 and 1 and so all that is required is to re-scale the random numbers to the interval [a,b]. This is done using the following equation (which can also be derived using the cumulative probability function),

$$x = a + (b - a)r \qquad (2.2)$$

where,

r is the random number between 0 and 1 used for the selection;
x is the resulting value chosen from the U[a,b] distribution.

For many distributions, the cumulative distribution function either cannot be written analytically or cannot be manipulated easily and so more complex methods have to be used. These are beyond the scope of this book but further information can be found in Press *et al.*(1992) and Pidd (1998).

2.4.3 Random number streams

It is essential to control properly the way that random numbers are used in a simulation model. For example, when a simulation contains several different sources of variability (such as inter-arrival times and the times using the ATM) the same random numbers should not be used for more than one purpose, otherwise this will create artificial relationships between the values used. Each time a new value is required a new random number should be chosen.

The simplest approach is to initialize the random number generator at the start of the simulation and then call the generator each time a new random number is required for whatever purpose. The simulation will then use a single sequence, or stream, of random numbers. The first number might determine the arrival time of the first customer and the second might determine the time spent using the ATM.

However, many software packages also allow each different part of the simulation to use a different random number stream. Each part of the simulation effectively has its own dedicated random number generator and each of these is initialized with a different seed. This is useful because it can make experimenting with the model more powerful when comparing alternative strategies. The use of different streams allows the random numbers used when running the model with the first strategy to be used as far as possible when running the model with the second strategy, so that the difference in the results is mainly due to the difference in strategy rather than differences in the random numbers used.

For example, a model of a production line may compare the existing line with the effect of adding one machine of a particular type. Variability in the model may arise in the processing times of all the machines, in the schedule of the parts being manufactured, in the testing of parts (which ones are rejected), in the times at which the machines break down and in the times to repair the machines. Having separate random number streams for each of these factors enables the same random numbers to be used for them in both experiments. Hence, the two configurations will be compared under more or less the same conditions, that is, the same parts schedule, the same breakdowns of the machines, and so on. The only difference is therefore the additional machine. This means that if there is a difference in performance due to adding the machine it is more likely to show up as statistically significant in the simulation results. However, if a single random number stream was used, the same conditions would not apply to both strategies in the corresponding runs because some of the random numbers would be needed for the processing times and breakdown times of the new machine. This alters what the random numbers in the stream would be used for (for example, a random number previously used for repair time of a machine might now be used for the testing of a part).

The use of the same random numbers for different strategies is called the common random numbers method. It is one of a family of variance reduction methods, so called because they can reduce the variations in the comparison of different strategies over several runs. Information on other methods of variance reduction is given in Section 5.3.1.

2.4.4 Random number tables

In order to run the manual simulation in Section 2.7, we will generate random numbers by hand using a random number table, which is a table of random digits. Such a table is given in Table 2.6, which was in fact obtained by taking the first digits from numbers produced by a Numerical Recipes (Press *et al.*, 1992) random number generator. Each digit should be treated as a separate random digit. They are grouped in pairs just to improve readability.

The table can be used to generate numbers between 0 and 1 by taking a certain number of digits and putting a decimal point in front. The number of digits used just needs to be enough to produce the precision required in the value being selected. Four digits will be sufficient in most cases. The first three random numbers produced in this way from Table 2.6 would be 0.1869, 0.8478 and 0.8578. The resulting values generated from a negative exponential with mean 6, using equation 2.1, would be 1.2, 11.3 and 11.7.

Table 2.6 Table of random digits

18 69 84 78 85	78 40 23 95 76	25 95 56 64 60	42 00 73 31 81
90 42 07 45 05	09 10 69 83 27	70 64 00 92 80	27 65 93 61 90
11 39 93 93 42	79 66 70 64 54	55 97 45 93 57	46 51 39 08 27
04 02 90 28 57	73 45 00 38 10	08 36 56 79 91	92 64 23 92 21
65 24 30 11 76	54 46 08 85 95	59 21 26 92 89	23 20 24 21 08
88 63 38 47 22	37 45 12 47 25	45 53 05 79 92	85 46 48 38 26
74 93 50 70 37	68 52 43 50 10	36 62 39 24 61	80 08 23 98 04
59 92 61 13 70	70 79 38 76 86	82 30 60 12 34	76 19 15 88 10
95 66 35 30 81	02 03 39 76 82	26 91 97 90 90	28 78 51 47 95
58 06 82 95 26	00 91 28 99 34	75 52 06 56 10	00 78 27 19 79
90 56 88 94 82	19 68 54 54 98	00 71 90 39 38	62 92 18 35 37
50 92 45 85 29	60 06 35 25 38	93 57 56 68 37	80 61 81 40 99
20 35 55 39 34	20 96 86 55 69	41 42 41 54 52	17 55 95 12 49
16 68 04 81 03	26 88 36 81 77	16 19 06 50 93	81 30 91 40 08
70 85 24 45 64	03 96 99 32 33	14 81 41 83 41	05 94 10 63 13
36 30 41 26 27	32 90 51 74 28	70 73 67 08 14	48 31 32 52 84
11 95 80 73 74	39 94 06 80 61	79 09 79 20 20	67 50 82 79 87
76 24 89 95 31	71 81 97 34 73	04 99 15 94 06	23 04 16 34 38
18 51 46 37 70	29 79 68 10 70	04 57 74 48 89	84 53 50 25 95
39 17 80 58 79	57 36 78 29 29	54 92 20 18 75	47 98 33 96 34
62 20 18 35 83	22 82 81 06 52	00 27 64 37 42	64 89 01 73 58
32 79 82 90 36	87 53 33 10 99	80 52 18 36 66	78 59 55 69 58
17 90 70 55 04	39 65 20 06 36	48 15 67 66 25	62 09 92 71 29
41 72 55 75 33	63 42 62 06 73	51 84 09 33 02	55 64 72 35 89
99 09 48 09 27	86 56 90 23 89	77 72 78 94 95	33 23 23 54 43

As an alternative to converting the digits into a number between 0 and 1, discrete data can be chosen directly by assigning certain digits to each category. The number of digits assigned is proportional to the required probability of selection. An example is given in Table 2.7.

Table 2.7 Assigning random digits to select values from a distribution

Value	*Probability*	*Random digits*
10	1/7	1
15	3/7	2,3,4
20	2/7	5,6
25	1/7	7

Reading a single digit from the random number table chooses the value. If the digit was 5, for example, the value used would be 20. Digits 8, 9 and 0 are ignored and the next digit in the table used.

Data from an empirical distribution can also be sampled in this way. Table 2.8 shows an example distribution of the number of specialized repair staff required to repair a machine for a sample of 95 breakdowns. This can be sampled by taking groups of two digits from the random number table to give a random number between 1 and 100 (taking 00 to be 100). The random numbers are then allocated according to the frequencies, as shown in Table 2.8. Therefore, the numbers 01–95 are used, with the first 53 allocated to the value 1, the next 33 to the value 2, and the last 9 to the value 3. Numbers 96, 97, 98, 99 and 00 are ignored. The first three numbers from the random number table (Table 2.6) are 18, 69, 84 which choose the values 1, 2, 2 respectively. This is called the top hat method because it is like pulling tickets at random out of a hat. The allocation of random numbers can be done in any way that is proportional to the frequency. Hence, when the proportions in each category are round values they can be used. For example, the empirical data in Table 2.3

Table 2.8 Top hat method

No. of repair staff	*Frequency*	*Random numbers*
1	53	01–53
2	33	54–86
3	9	87–95

could be sampled from the random number table using random numbers 01–10, 11–38, 39–83 and 84–00 for the four categories respectively (following the proportions in Table 2.4).

Note that we can start from any point in the table. In fact, the equivalent to random number streams (Section 2.4.3) with a random number table is to use different parts of the table for each source of variability. For example the table could be split for two sources by using different halves of the table for each source or by using alternate lines.

2.5 Three-phase simulation executive

The simulation executive is the part of the simulation that provides overall control. It is the architecture that carries out the simulation run using the entities, states and events input by the user to describe the model, along with random numbers from the random number generator.

Since a simulation run consists of a series of events, the executive has to carry out a repeating process of finding what the next event will be and the time at which it will occur, advancing the simulation clock to that time and then implementing the event. The details of the event will tell the executive what changes to make to the state of the system and what future events to add to the event list. The executive always keeps a record of the current state of the system and is responsible for producing the output statistics requested by the user.

The potentially difficult organizational task that the executive has to perform is to find the event that will happen next. This is made easier by using the event list. The event list keeps a record of the next events that can be scheduled for each entity. The event list looks one step ahead for each entity and no further. For example, it would be possible to calculate the arrival times of all the customers in the ATM simulation by choosing all the inter-arrival times at the start. Instead, just the arrival of the first customer will be scheduled on the event list at the start. When the first customer arrives, the arrival of the second customer will then be added to the event list, and so on.

The event list records the scheduled events and the times at which they will occur. To find the next event, the executive just has to look through this list and find the earliest time. Events are added to the list when a previous event takes place, using the event details information (Section 2.3.3). Whenever an event is performed it will be deleted from the list. The event list needs to specify the entity if an event could refer to more than one entity (for example, the entry for *finish using machine* would need to say which ATM if there were two ATMs). Part of executing the events may include using the random number generator to determine which path the entity takes or the time at which a future event will be scheduled (by choosing the duration of an activity).

There are three reasons why the event list looks just one step ahead. Firstly, this reduces the amount of information that the simulation executive has to record and sort through. Secondly, for most entities it is not possible to determine what will happen beyond the next event without actually carrying out the simulation, because of the interactions between the entities. Thirdly, it allows the simulation to run without specifying an end time. The simulation can be started and allowed to run until the user stops it.

Only the bound events can actually be scheduled in advance – conditional events have to wait until their conditions are met. This means that whenever a bound event occurs the simulation executive must also check through all the conditional events to see if the conditions for any of these events are now satisfied. If they are, then the conditional event is also performed before the simulation clock is advanced further. A conditional event may also trigger other conditional events and so they must all be repeatedly checked through until a point is reached when none of the conditional events can be carried out.

This way of organizing the processing of events is called the three-phase approach and was originally devised by Tocher (1963). The first phase, the 'A' phase, consists of finding the next event and advancing the simulation clock to that time. The second 'B' phase is carrying out all the bound (or B) events due at that time, and the third 'C' phase is carrying out all the conditional (or C) events whose conditions are satisfied. Figure 2.6 shows a flowchart of the complete three-phase simulation executive.

There may be more than one event scheduled to take place at the same time. This can happen either when there is more than one bound event on the event list with the same time of occurrence or when more than one conditional event is triggered at the same time by the bound events. The simulation therefore needs to decide the order in which to perform these events and this can have a significant effect on the results. In the case of the bound events, all those scheduled to take place at the current time are performed in the B phase. However, for some bound events the changes in state can depend on the current state of some part of the system, and this may in turn depend on whether the other bound events occur before or after.

The order in which conditional events are performed can also be very important in some simulations. This can happen when entities are competing for scarce resources with the first conditional event getting the resource and preventing the second conditional event from occurring (because its conditions are no longer satisfied). For example, if there are two separate queues to use a single item the chosen queue will be the one that can proceed. An example of this is a weighbridge for collection or delivery of materials by lorry. The lorries are weighed when they arrive and when they leave, with the weight difference being the amount delivered or collected. Queues can therefore arise of both arriving and departing lorries. If arriving lorries are given priority, for example, long queues of departing lorries will tend to build up. This could even block the system if the site runs out of space so that the arriving lorries cannot enter. Another example is a travel agent, with a queue of customers and a ringing telephone, who has to decide whether to serve the customers in the agency or the phone customers. In these situations the user can specify a priority for each event when building the model. This can include a dynamic condition such as a higher priority for the longer queue. In the absence of such information the simulation executive will simply perform the first of the conditional events that it finds whose conditions are satisfied.

The main tasks of the executive are therefore to maintain a record of the current system state, search the event list for the next event, and update the state and event list when each event takes place. From a computing point of view, it is important both for the information to be recorded in a concise way and for the list of events to be searched efficiently if the simulation is to run as quickly as possible. Ways of organizing and searching this information in different computing languages are beyond the scope of this book but are discussed elsewhere, in Banks *et al.* (1996) for example.

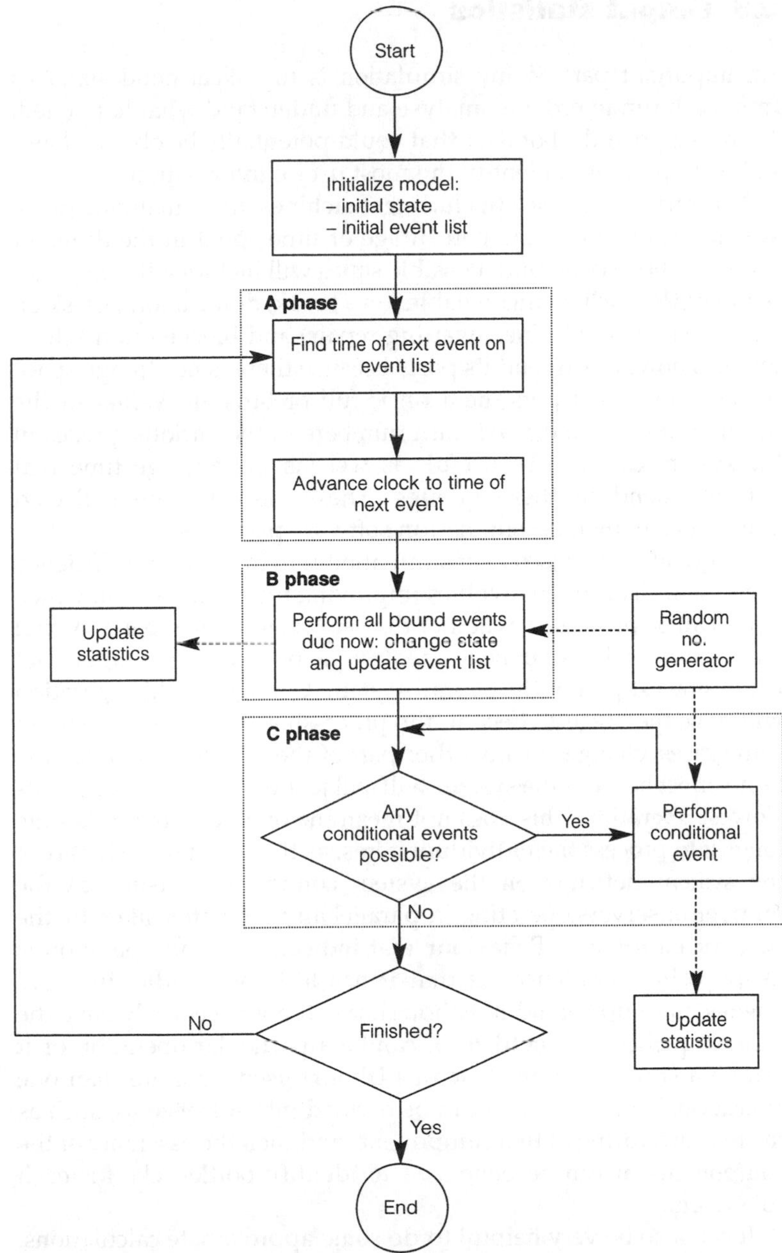

Figure 2.6 Three-phase simulation executive procedure

2.6 Output statistics

An important part of any simulation is to collect good statistics from each run in order to analyse and understand what happened. There is a great deal of data that could potentially be obtained and so it is important to identify the most useful information.

For serving entities (including machines in a manufacturing system), statistics on the percentage of time spent in the different states can be very helpful. Possible states will include idle and busy, but may also include unavailable (on a break, doing another task or, in the case of a machine, awaiting repair) and blocked (a machine that has nowhere to send its parts because there is no storage space or the conveyor it puts them on is full or broken). Values of the mean, minimum and maximum numbers in the various queues in the system can also be useful, as well as the average time that entities spend in these queues. These statistics are collected automatically by most simulation software packages.

Frequently, an objective of simulation is to improve the efficiency of a system. This often involves improving the overall rate at which items can be processed, whether they are customers or parts. A vital part of this analysis can be to identify the bottleneck operation that is the slowest part of the overall system. Changes to this operation will have the biggest effect on the processing rate of the system. In some cases, changes to any other part of the system will have little or no effect because the system will still just work at the speed of its slowest operation. This does not mean the operation that takes the longest to process the individual items, as the speed of each part of the system depends on the system configuration (such as the number of servers operating in parallel and the paths taken by the parts or customers). Behaviour that indicates that an operation is likely to be a bottleneck is that it has little or no idle time and queues build up behind it, although it will not necessarily have the biggest queues. The bottleneck can be a particular operation or it can be a scarce resource (such as labour) used by more than one operation. Where a system can be divided into subsystems, such as the manufacturing of two components and then the assembly of the components, it can be beneficial to identify bottlenecks for each subsystem.

It can also be very helpful to do some approximate calculations. Although it is dangerous to use average values in a simulation model rather than model the variability, calculations using averages can give a preliminary insight into the system. For example, if the average rate of customer arrivals is greater than the average service rate of the server, then the system will not be able to cope and queues will inevitably build up. The variability in the system can only exacerbate this. It is possible to include a wide range of factors into such calculations (Brooks and Tobias, 2000). Time spent in gaining an initial understanding of the system in this way rather than going straight into detailed experimentation can be extremely beneficial.

When experimentation is carried out (Section 4.5), the information that will be most useful to the user depends on the purpose of the modelling project. The information required may change as the project progresses and existing results are investigated. However, a great deal of time can be saved by a good choice of statistics and by automating this process as much as possible. It is particularly helpful if summary statistics can be collected automatically by the simulation when several runs are performed together.

2.7 Hand simulation case study

The best way to gain an understanding of how a simulation model works overall is do a simulation by hand. A comparison with a hand simulation is also a good test of whether a computer simulation has been built correctly – if the same random numbers are used the behaviour should be identical. In a hand simulation we take the role of the simulation executive, following the step by step procedure of Figure 2.6.

This section presents a hand simulation of an extended model of the bank. This time, we will model the following description of what happens inside the bank:

The bank opens at 9 am and closes at 5 pm. Customers arrive at random at an average rate of 40 customers per hour. Two bank tellers are on duty throughout the day to serve the customers – a junior and a senior teller. The senior teller, being more experienced, is quicker at serving the customers. If the number of people queueing to be served reaches three then an additional senior teller, working elsewhere in the bank, comes on duty. The additional teller goes off duty if, at the end of serving a customer, the queue is one or zero. Around half the customers are personal customers making a deposit to their accounts and the serving times for these customers are quite short. The remainder of the customers includes business customers paying in their takings, customers with queries on their accounts, new customers opening accounts and customers collecting foreign currency for holidays abroad. The serving time for most of these customers is much longer. As a result the distribution of serving times has two peaks and data collected shows the following:

Table 2.9 Bank teller serving times

Serving time (mins)	*Proportion for junior*	*Proportion for senior*
1–2	0.05	0.10
2–3	0.10	0.25
3–4	0.20	0.15
4–5	0.15	0.15
5–6	0.20	0.20
6–7	0.15	0.15
7–8	0.07	
8–9	0.05	
9–10	0.03	

The bank wants to predict the waiting times of customers and to compare this with other ways of organizing the system.

We can do some preliminary analysis of this system by calculating the average serving times of the junior and the senior, which are 5.01 mins and 4.05 mins respectively (assuming times are evenly distributed within each interval so that the mean for the interval 1–2 is 1.5 mins, and so on). Therefore, if the junior and senior are busy all of the time they will serve about 12 and 15 customers per hour on average, in other words a total of 27 customers per hour. With the additional teller this can increase to 42 customers per hour. Since the customer arrival rate is 40 per hour, it is clear that the additional teller will be required most of the time, although the pattern of work and of the customers' waiting times is not clear. A simulation model will allow these to be estimated as well as allowing changes to the system to be tried out.

There are three stages involved in implementing the simulation, which are described in Sections 2.7.1 – 2.7.3 respectively. The first is to specify the entities, states, events and event details. The second is to set up the way that the random numbers will be used to simulate variability. The third is to run the simulation. Section 2.7.4 then explores how this model could be used in practice.

2.7.1 Simulation specification

In order to simulate this system, we must decide what the entities, states and events are. In fact, these are very similar to the ATM example. The entities again are the customers and the servers, although here the servers are human rather than a machine. The customers follow the same sequence of events as that shown in Table 2.1, except that the descriptions need changing as the customers are now being served rather than using the machine, and so on. As mentioned in Section 2.3.3, the fact that there are two servers rather than one makes very little difference.

The behaviour of the additional teller in becoming on and off duty does add an additional complication compared to the ATM example. An activity cycle diagram can help to show the events needed to implement this behaviour. The activity cycle diagram for the bank is shown in Figure 2.7. Compared to the activity diagram for the ATM example (Figure 2.5) this has a state added for the additional teller being off duty and the arrows have been annotated to show the conditions for becoming on and off duty.

The customer experiences the same three basic events as for the ATM example of arriving, starting being served and finishing being served. The event for starting serving also affects the tellers by changing the state of the teller used to *busy*. The presence of two arrows for the tellers on the activity cycle diagram into the *being served* state shows that there are two possible conditions. One applies to tellers that are in the state *idle* and one to the additional teller when *off-duty*. Since there are two conditions, the easiest way to do this is to have two conditional events for starting serving, which we have called *start serve* and *start serve on duty*. (Another way would be to have a single event with two alternative conditions but the logic of this event would be rather complicated). The *start serve* event needs to specify which teller the customer goes to if there is a choice of tellers. Here, the order senior, junior, additional will be assumed. There is a chance that both conditional events may be able to take place at the same time, in which case we shall assume that the *start serve* event has the higher priority.

The bound event to finish serving can change the state of the

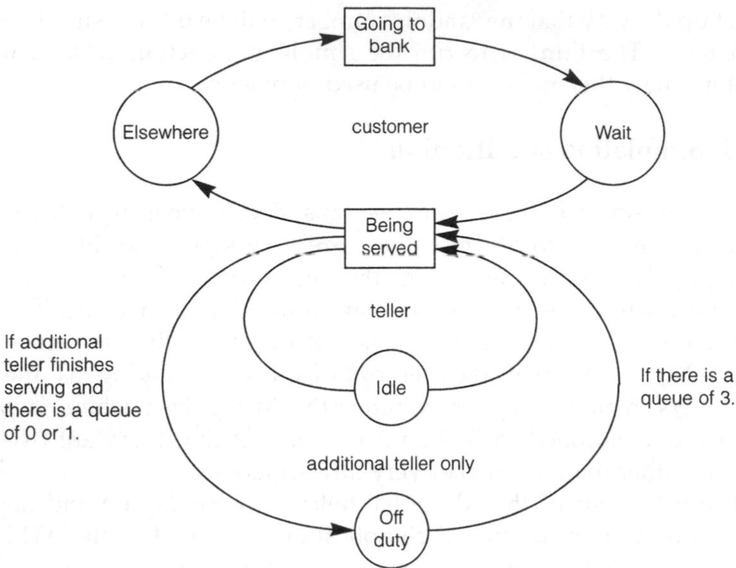

Figure 2.7 Bank activity cycle diagram

additional teller to either *idle* or *off-duty*. This depends on the number of customers in the queue when the event occurs and so the state changes for this event includes these alternatives. The order of the bound events could also be important. If the additional teller finishes serving at the same time as an arrival takes place, the number in the queue used to determine whether the teller goes off-duty will depend on whether the arrival event is performed before or after. We shall assume that the arrival event takes place last and that if several tellers finish serving at the same time their bound events are performed in the order they appear on the event list. The event details are shown in Table 2.10.

2.7.2 Use of random numbers

Once the events have been specified, the other aspect of the simulation to set up is the way that the random numbers are going to be used for the variability. There are two sources of variability, the inter-arrival times of the customers and the service times. The random nature of the arrivals means that the negative exponential applies for the inter-arrival times with a mean, here, of 1.5 mins.

Using equation 2.1, the times are given by:

$$\text{inter-arrival time} = -1.5\ln(1-r) \quad (2.3)$$

where r is a random number between 0 and 1.

Table 2.10 Event details for the bank simulation

Event	***Type***	***Conditions for event to occur***	***Change in state caused by event***	***Future events to schedule***
Arrival	Bound		Add new customer to end of queue with state *waiting*	Next *arrival* (by choosing an inter-arrival time)
Start serve	Conditional	There is a customer waiting and at least one teller is *idle*.	Change state of customer at front of waiting queue from state *waiting* to state *being served*. Choose teller from those that are *idle* with priority senior, junior, additional, and change state of teller to *busy*.	*Finish serve* (by choosing the service time)
Start serve on duty	Conditional	The additional teller is *off-duty* and there are 3 people waiting	Change state of customer at front of waiting queue from state *waiting* to state *being served*. Change state of additional teller from *off-duty* to *busy*.	*Finish serve* (by choosing the service time)
Finish serve	Bound		Change state of customer from *being served* to *elsewhere*. If teller is the additional teller and the queue is less than two then change state of teller from *busy* to *off-duty*. Otherwise change state of teller from *busy* to *idle*.	

It is also necessary to decide the precision to which time will be recorded in the simulation. Equation 2.3 will give a decimal answer and it is easier to work in decimals rather than to have to convert everything to seconds (although a simulation software package should do this). One decimal place is probably sufficient detail so that we are working to the nearest 1/10 of a minute (that is, the nearest six seconds). Then four random digits will be sufficient. For example, starting at the top of Table 2.6 gives a random number of 0.1869. Using equation 2.3 gives an inter-arrival time of 0.3 mins (that is, 18 secs). If r is very small, then the inter-arrival time from equation 2.3 may be 0.0 to one decimal place. Since the inter-arrival time should always be positive, a value of 0.1 mins will be used in these circumstances.

The top-hat method (Section 2.4.4) can be used to sample the serving times. Taking two random digits gives a random number between 1 and 100 and these can be allocated according to the proportions in Table 2.9. The allocations are shown in Table 2.11.

Table 2.11 Random numbers for bank teller serving times

Serving time (minutes)	*Random numbers for junior*	*Random numbers for senior*
1–2	01–05	01–10
2–3	06–15	11–35
3–4	16–35	36–50
4–5	36–50	51–65
5–6	51–70	66–85
6–7	71–85	86–00
7–8	86–92	
8–9	93–97	
9–10	98–00	

This allocation chooses a serving time interval of width one minute (for example, 2–3 mins). It is then necessary to choose a time at random within this interval. We will assume that times are uniformly distributed over this interval. Then, all that is needed is a random number between 0 and 1 which can be obtained by taking some digits and putting a decimal point in front. The precision of the simulation is one decimal place of minutes and so, strictly, two digits should be chosen and then rounded. If just one digit was used, the serving times would be slightly under-estimated (since 0 would choose the lower end of the interval but the upper end would never be chosen).

Taking the third row of the random number table (Table 2.6), for instance, the first two digits, 11, choose the time interval. For the junior this would be 2–3 mins. The next two digits, 39, give the time after the decimal point so that the time is 2.39 mins, rounded to 2.4 mins.

A single stream of random numbers will be used starting at the beginning of Table 2.6. So, whenever random digits are required the next ones in the table will be used. Separate streams (Section 2.4.3) could be used by, for instance, using row 1 for inter-arrival times, rows 2 – 4 for the serving times for the three servers respectively, row 5 for more inter-arrival times, and so on.

2.7.3 Simulation run

Now that the event details and the random sampling have been set up, the simulation run can start. This requires taking the role of the simulation executive and following the procedure in Figure 2.6.

The executive maintains the current state of the system and the current event list and so these need to be recorded in a suitable way. There is no standard way to lay out a hand simulation. The detail required for the system state depends on the detail to which the entities are to be modelled (Section 2.3.1). Here, the states of the individual items will be represented. In a system like this with a main entity, the customers, passing through a series of queues and activities, the system state can be maintained by keeping a record of each queue and activity. The event list is simply a list of the scheduled events and the time at which each will occur. We will set out the system state and event list as shown in Table 2.12.

Table 2.12 Layout for system state and event list

		State			Statistics
Time	*Queue*	*Senior*	*Junior*	*Additional*	*Queue time*

Event list			Random numbers
Event	*Time*	*Done*	

A column has been added to the state table to record the output statistic of the queueing time for each customer. In the event list, the events will be ticked in the 'done' column once they have been implemented. It is useful to record the random numbers used, both for reference and to keep track of where we are in the random number table (it can also be helpful to cross off the numbers used in the table).

This section will explain, step by step, the procedure for a single run of the bank model. The best way to follow what is happening is to draw your own tables for the system state and event list using the layout shown in Table 2.12. Draw the two tables side by side as shown rather than above each other to give space for plenty of states and events. Then fill in the tables as the procedure is explained below. Once you understand what is happening, try and complete the tables for each step before the step is explained in the text.

The simulation procedure consists of following Figure 2.6. The first step in Figure 2.6 is to initialize the model by deciding the initial state and event list. The bank simulation starts at 9 am, which we will call time = 0, with no customers in the bank. The initial state is therefore as shown in Table 2.13.

Table 2.13 Initial system state

State					Statistics
Time	*Queue*	*Senior*	*Junior*	*Additional*	*Queue time*
0.0	empty	idle	idle	off-duty	

The second part of initializing the model is to generate the initial event list. This needs to record all events that can be scheduled at the start of the simulation. There must be at least one such event to enable the simulation to proceed. Here, the only event that can be scheduled is the arrival of the first customer. The first four random digits in Table 2.6 are used (as 0.1869) to determine the inter-arrival time of the first customer as 0.3 mins (using equation 2.3). The initial event list is shown in Table 2.14.

Table 2.14 Initial event list

Event list			Random numbers
Event	*Time*	*Done*	
Arrival C1	0.3		18 69

The event list gives the name of the event and the customer it affects, with C1 denoting customer number one.

The model is now initialized and so the simulation proceeds by going round the loop of A phase, B phase and C phase until the end of the run (Figure 2.6). The A phase is to find the time of the next event on the event list and to advance the clock to that time. There is only one event on the event list at the moment, and so the clock can be advanced to its time of 0.3.

The B phase can then take place by performing the event due at this time following the event details set up in Table 2.10. For the arrival of C1, this means changing the state of the system by adding C1 to the queue and scheduling the next arrival. The next four digits in the random number table, 84 78, give the inter-arrival time of customer C2 as 2.8 mins. The current time is 0.3 and so this customer will arrive at time 3.1. The state and event list after the B phase are therefore as shown in Table 2.15.

Table 2.15 Simulation after the first B phase

State					Statistics
Time	*Queue*	*Senior*	*Junior*	*Additional*	*Queue time*
0.0	empty	idle	idle	off-duty	
0.3	C1	idle	idle	off-duty	

Event list			Random numbers
Event	*Time*	*Done*	
Arrival C1	0.3	✓	18 69
Arrival C2	3.1		84 78

After the B phase we must check each of the conditional events to see whether their conditions are satisfied. There are only two conditional events, *start serve* and *start serve on duty*. Since C1 is queueing and both tellers are idle, the conditions apply for the *start serve* event and so this event needs to be performed. Following Table 2.10, the customer needs to be moved from the queue and to start being served by the senior, and the *finish serve* event needs to be scheduled. The random digits 85 select the serving time interval from Table 2.11 as 5 – 6 mins, and the next digits, 78, give the exact value of 5.78 mins, rounded to 5.8 mins. As the current time is 0.3, *finish serve* is scheduled at time 6.1 mins. The state and event list after the C phase are shown in Table 2.16.

The event list notes the server to which the *finish serve* event applies by S, J or A for the senior, junior and additional servers respectively. The statistics column records that C1 did not have to wait to be served.

Table 2.16 Simulation after the first C phase

State					Statistics	Event list			Random numbers
Time	*Queue*	*Senior*	*Junior*	*Additional*	*Queue time*	*Event*	*Time*	*Done*	
0.0	empty	idle	idle	off-duty		Arrival C1	0.3	✓	18 69
0.3	C1	idle	idle	off-duty		Arrival C2	3.1		84 78
0.3	empty	C1	idle	off-duty	0.0	Finish serve S	6.1		85 78

None of the conditional events can now be performed and so the simulation procedure returns to the A phase. There are now two outstanding events on the event list with the earliest being the *arrival* C2 event due at time 3.1. So, the clock is advanced to time 3.1. The B phase then takes place with this event being performed. As before, this involves adding the customer to the queue and scheduling the next arrival using the next random numbers, 40 23. This gives an inter-arrival time of 0.8 mins and, since the current time is 3.1 mins, the next arrival will occur at time 3.9 mins. Table 2.17 shows the simulation now.

Table 2.17 Simulation after the second B phase

State					Statistics	Event list			Random numbers
Time	*Queue*	*Senior*	*Junior*	*Additional*	*Queue time*	*Event*	*Time*	*Done*	
0.0	empty	idle	idle	off-duty		Arrival C1	0.3	✓	18 69
0.3	C1	idle	idle	off-duty		Arrival C2	3.1	✓	84 78
0.3	empty	C1	idle	off-duty	0.0	Finish serve S	6.1		85 78
3.1	C2	C1	idle	off-duty		Arrival C3	3.9		40 23

In the second C phase, the *start serve* event can again be performed since C2 is queueing and the junior teller is idle. So the junior starts serving C2 and the *finish serve J* event is added to the event list. Random numbers 95 and 76 give a serving time of 8.8 mins and so the *finish serve J* event is due at time 11.9. No more conditional events can then be performed. Table 2.18 shows the simulation at this stage.

Returning to the A phase, the next event on the event list is the arrival of customer three at time 3.9. In the B phase, as before, the customer is added to the queue and the arrival of the next customer (C4) is scheduled 0.5 mins later (using 0.2595) at time 4.4. You can update your tables by recording the new state at time 3.9 with C3 in the queue and by adding *arrival* C4 to the event list. *Arrival* C3 can be ticked as done. No conditional events can be performed this time in the C phase since the two tellers are busy and the conditions

Table 2.18 Simulation after the second C phase

State					Statistics	Event list			Random numbers
Time	*Queue*	*Senior*	*Junior*	*Additional*	*Queue time*	*Event*	*Time*	*Done*	
0.0	empty	idle	idle	off-duty		Arrival C1	0.3	✓	18 69
0.3	C1	idle	idle	off-duty		Arrival C2	3.1	✓	84 78
0.3	empty	C1	idle	off-duty	0.0	Finish serve S	6.1		85 78
3.1	C2	C1	idle	off-duty		Arrival C3	3.9		40 23
3.1	empty	C1	C2	off-duty	0.0	Finish serve J	11.9		95 76

are not satisfied for the additional teller to become on-duty.

The same procedure is followed in the next cycle as the arrival of customer four is the next event and again no conditional events can be performed. Using random number 0.5664, the arrival of customer five is scheduled at time 5.7 (4.4 + 1.3). Again, the state and event list need to be updated.

In the next cycle, the customer arrival (of C5) is again the next event, at time 5.7. So the clock is advanced to time 5.7, the customer is added to the queue and the arrival of C6 is scheduled. The simulation after this B phase is shown in Table 2.19.

Table 2.19 Simulation after the arrival of C5 at time 5.7

State					Statistics	Event list			Random numbers
Time	*Queue*	*Senior*	*Junior*	*Additional*	*Queue time*	*Event*	*Time*	*Done*	
0.0	empty	idle	idle	off-duty		Arrival C1	0.3	✓	18 69
0.3	C1	idle	idle	off-duty		Arrival C2	3.1	✓	84 78
0.3	empty	C1	idle	off-duty	0.0	Finish serve S	6.1		85 78
3.1	C2	C1	idle	off-duty		Arrival C3	3.9	✓	40 23
3.1	empty	C1	C2	off-duty	0.0	Finish serve J	11.9		95 76
3.9	C3	C1	C2	off-duty		Arrival C4	4.4	✓	25 95
4.4	C4,C3	C1	C2	off-duty		Arrival C5	5.7	✓	56 64
5.7	C5,C4,C3	C1	C2	off-duty		Arrival C6	7.1		60 42

As there are now three customers queueing, the conditions for the *start serve on duty* event are now satisfied. Therefore the C phase performs this event by bringing the additional teller on duty to serve C3 and by scheduling the finishing time of the service. The next random numbers 00 73 are used for the serving time, giving a time of 6.7 mins so that *finish serve A* can be added to the event list with a time 12.4. With no more conditional events possible the C phase ends. For simplicity, Table 2.20 shows just the current state and the outstanding events on the event list. Customer C3 arrived at time 3.9 and so spent 1.8 mins queueing before being served.

Table 2.20 Simulation after the C phase at time 5.7

State					Statistics
Time	*Queue*	*Senior*	*Junior*	*Additional*	*Queue time*
5.7	C5,C4	C1	C2	C3	1.8

Event list			Random numbers
Event	*Time*	*Done*	
Finish serve S	6.1		85 78
Finish serve J	11.9		95 76
Arrival C6	7.1		60 42
Finish serve A	12.4		00 73

The next event on the event list is *finish serve S* at time 6.1 and so the clock is advanced to 6.1 and the event performed. This just causes the senior to become *idle* as customer one leaves the bank. In the C phase, since the senior is idle and there are customers waiting, *start serve S* can take place. Therefore, the senior starts serving customer four and the *finish serve S* event for this customer is scheduled at time 8.9 using random numbers 31 81. No more conditional events can occur and the system state and event list after this C phase are shown in Table 2.21.

Table 2.21 Simulation after the C phase at time 6.1

State					Statistics
Time	*Queue*	*Senior*	*Junior*	*Additional*	*Queue time*
6.1	C5,C4	idle	C2	C3	
6.1	C5	C4	C2	C3	1.7

Event list			Random numbers
Event	*Time*	*Done*	
Finish serve J	11.9		95 76
Arrival C6	7.1		60 42
Finish serve A	12.4		00 73
Finish serve S	8.9		31 81

The simulation run continues in this way through the cycle of the three-phase procedure until the end of the run. The end point of this simulation will be when the bank closes after a simulation time of 480 mins, unless the user stops the simulation earlier. Table 2.22 shows the first 15 mins. The additional teller goes off-duty at time 12.4 because when the teller finished serving the customer the queue was less than two (in fact, no customers were waiting).

2.7.4 Ways of using the model

This hand simulation is just the start of a single run of the model. The model run begins with the bank containing no customers. The first two customers to arrive at the bank in the morning will never have to queue and it will take a little while for queues to build up (in this particular run they happen to build up quite quickly). The

Table 2.22 Simulation for the first 15 minutes

State					Statistics
Time	*Queue*	*Senior*	*Junior*	*Additional*	*Queue time*
0.0	empty	idle	idle	off-duty	
0.3	C1	idle	idle	off-duty	
0.3	empty	C1	idle	off-duty	0.0
3.1	C2	C1	idle	off-duty	
3.1	empty	C1	C2	off-duty	0.0
3.9	C3	C1	C2	off-duty	
4.4	C4,C3	C1	C2	off-duty	
5.7	C5,C4,C3	C1	C2	off-duty	
5.7	C5,C4	C1	C2	C3	1.8
6.1	C5,C4	idle	C2	C3	
6.1	C5	C4	C2	C3	1.7
7.1	C6,C5	C4	C2	C3	
8.9	C6,C5	idle	C2	C3	
8.9	C6	C5	C2	C3	3.2
10.4	C6	idle	C2	C3	
10.4	empty	C6	C2	C3	3.3
10.6	C7	C6	C2	C3	
10.8	C8,C7	C6	C2	C3	
11.5	C8,C7	idle	C2	C3	
11.5	C8	C7	C2	C3	0.9
11.9	C8	C7	idle	C3	
11.9	empty	C7	C8	C3	1.1
12.4	empty	C7	C8	off-duty	
13.5	C9	C7	C8	off-duty	

Event list			Random numbers
Event	*Time*	*Done*	
Arrival C1	0.3	✓	18 69
Arrival C2	3.1	✓	84 78
Finish serve S	6.1	✓	85 78
Arrival C3	3.9	✓	40 23
Finish serve J	11.9	✓	95 76
Arrival C4	4.4	✓	25 95
Arrival C5	5.7	✓	56 64
Arrival C6	7.1	✓	60 42
Finish serve A	12.4	✓	00 73
Finish serve S	8.9	✓	31 81
Arrival C7	10.6	✓	90 42
Finish serve S	10.4	✓	07 45
Finish serve S	11.5	✓	05 09
Arrival C8	10.8	✓	10 69
Arrival C9	13.5	✓	83 27
Finish serve S	17.1		70 64
Finish serve J	21.8		00.92
Arrival C10	15.9		80 27

start of the simulation will therefore not be typical of the behaviour during the rest of the day and this needs to be taken into account in analysing the results. A single run of the model is also not sufficient to draw general conclusions about the behaviour of the system. The results depend on the particular random numbers used and so several runs with different random numbers need to be performed. The way to experiment with a simulation model and then analyse the results are discussed in Section 4.5.

There are many different ways of organizing the queueing system at the bank that could be compared with the current system using the model. These include:

- Three or more tellers serving full time.
- More than one additional teller.
- A separate queue and dedicated teller for personal customers paying money into their accounts (this requires separate serving time distributions for the different types of customer).
- A separate teller for new accounts and enquiries about new services (the bank may consider that it is particularly important to serve potential new customers quickly).

- More training for junior tellers so that their serving time is closer to that of the seniors.
- Providing a machine to allow quick account deposits.

Thought also has to be given to the way of measuring the performance of the system. Perhaps the average queueing time of customers might be the performance measure or it may be more important to avoid customers having to queue for a long period of time (so the measure might be the proportion of customers queueing for more than three minutes, say). Perhaps a combination of these measures might be appropriate. The simulation also allows the workload and work pattern of each teller to be estimated. There may be other behaviour taking place in the system that could be important to model such as customers leaving the bank if they have to wait too long. The model could be expanded to include the ATM, which could be important if potential ATM customers use the bank when the ATM queue is long. Arrival rates are likely to vary during the day and this could also be included in the model.

Building a simulation model can be an excellent catalyst for generating ideas about the system. In theory it is possible to come up with the above ways of operating the bank and measuring performance without building a model. However, it is often the case that the process of formally describing the way the system works in a model enables weaknesses in the system and alternative approaches to be identified even before the model is experimented with. Improving one's understanding of the way the system works should always be an objective of simulation (Section 1.4).

2.8 Other simulation approaches

2.8.1 Alternatives to the three-phase approach

As well as the three-phase approach, there are other ways of constructing a discrete event simulation procedure, namely event, activity or process based approaches. These approaches all work on the same principle of modelling the system using entities and events and repeatedly searching for and executing the next event. The differences between the approaches are that the event details are organized slightly differently and, as a result, the precise tasks that the executive does are slightly different. Variations on these approaches are also possible. Only a very brief summary of the different approaches is provided here – a more detailed explanation and discussion can be found in Paul (1991) and Pidd (1998).

The event-based approach uses only bound events by incorporating the conditional state changes into each of the bound events that might cause them to happen. The event details therefore can be very complicated, making building and updating models more difficult than for the three-phase approach. However, as the executive does not perform a C phase such models tend to run faster.

The activity-based approach, on the other hand, treats all events as conditional events. Bound events under the three-phase approach are made into conditional events by applying the condition that the simulation time has to reach the time at which the event is scheduled. The executive does not have to perform a B phase but has to search all events at the C phase. This makes this approach rather slow and it is little used in practice.

In a process-based approach the events in the whole life cycle of each entity are explicitly expressed as a sequence. The approach is similar to the three-phase approach with bound and conditional events being separated. The difference is that when a bound event is due for an entity, the entity is moved as far as possible along its sequence of events. If bound events are due for several entities at the same time, a conditional event may therefore be performed for one entity before the other bound events (the three-phase approach performs all bound events first). Care is required with the specification of tasks and the order in which entities are progressed to avoid deadlock situations where the simulation stops because the entities are all waiting for each other to do something. However, the process-based approach is a natural approach for describing certain systems and is used quite a lot in simulation software.

An alternative approach to handling time in simulation is time-slicing whereby time is advanced in the simulation in equal increments rather than being advanced to the time of the next event. Rather than maintain an event list the simulation just looks to see whether any events can take place after each increment. However, most of the time no events can take place (for example, in the bank simulation the increment would have to be 0.1 mins) and so this approach is inefficient.

The main advantage of the three-phase approach is that it is the most flexible approach, being relatively easy to apply in most situations. It also tends to be easy to maintain and update models built in this way.

2.8.2 Simulating systems with a regular sequence of events

In some systems, events happen in a regular order and, in some cases, at regular times. The benefit when simulating such systems is that the simulation can often be done using a spreadsheet.

Stock control systems are an example of such a system. The delivery, sales and orders of stock can be simulated on a daily, weekly or monthly basis. Each row of the spreadsheet simulates the values for one time period and calculates the opening and closing stock for that period. Sampling from standard or empirical probability distributions enables variations in sales (both unpredictable variations from one time period to the next and regular seasonal trends) and variations in delivery lead times to be included in the model. This allows situations to be modelled and experimented with that would be very difficult to solve using a mathematical inventory control model (see Lewis: *Inventory Control*, in this volume).

It may also be the case that the events always take place in the same sequence even though they are not at regular times. For example, a shop could use spreadsheet simulation to estimate the change required in its tills (again, effectively stock control) by simulating the payment due and the amount tendered by each successive customer, even though the customers arrive at different times.

Financial planning and project appraisal under uncertainty can also often be simulated on a spreadsheet by sampling values from probability distributions.

2.9 Conclusion

Although discrete event simulation is used to model a wide variety of systems, the general methodology followed is always the same. The system is described as events and states along with rules for the occurrence of the events. Providing that the events have been properly specified, a systematic application of the simulation executive ensures that events are performed in the correct order. A random number generator is used to select values from probability distributions specified by the user to model variability. Finally, the model produces output statistics that the user can analyse.

References and further reading

Banks, J., Carson, J.S. and Nelson, B.L. (1996) *Discrete-Event System Simulation*, 2nd edn, Upper Saddle River, NJ: Prentice-Hall.

Brooks, R.J. and Tobias, A.M. (2000) 'Simplification in the Simulation of Manufacturing Systems', *International Journal of Production Research*, 38:5, 1009–27.

Dahl, O. and Nygaard, K. (1966) 'SIMULA: An Algol-based simulation language', *Communications of the ACM*, 9, 671–8.

Hills, P.R. (1971) *HOCUS*, Egham, UK: P-E Group.

Law, A.M. and Kelton, W.D. (2000) *Simulation Modeling and Analysis*, 3rd edn. New York: McGraw-Hill.

Paul, R.J. (1991) 'Recent Developments in Simulation Modelling', *Journal of the Operational Research Society*, 42:3, 217–26.

Pidd, M. (1998) *Computer Simulation in Management Science*, 4th edn. Chichester, UK: Wiley.

Press, W.H., Teukolsky, S.A., Vetterling, W.T. and Flannery, B.P. (1992) *Numerical Recipes in C: The Art of Scientific Computing*, 2nd edn. Cambridge University Press.

Schruben, L. (1983) 'Simulation Modelling with Event Graphs', *Communications of the ACM*, 26:11, 957–63.

Tocher, K.D. (1963) *The Art of Simulation*, London: English Universities Press.

3 Software for Simulation

3.1 Introduction

A typical simulation requires far more complexity than can be managed by 'hand', at least in a reasonable time-scale. As a result most simulations are performed using a computer. Physical simulations are an alternative approach, for instance, a child's railway set to model the operation of a station, but these would often take longer to build than computer simulations, and are probably more costly and less flexible. Consequently, they are rarely used.

For very simple models it may be possible to develop the simulation using a spreadsheet. When a more complex model is required, simulation modellers do not have to program their simulations from scratch, although, for various reasons, some may choose to do so. As with most other Operational Research techniques, specialist software is available to aid the development and use of models. Many of the simulation software packages that are now available have built-in facilities for visual interactive simulation (VIS) (Hurrion, 1976). The visual element provides an animated display of the running model. The interactive element enables the model user to interact with the running model, obtaining statistical reports and making changes to the model before running it further. Such software has the advantage that it provides a greater understanding of the model, aids model validation and experimentation, and acts as a powerful communication tool. Figure 3.1 shows a screen shot of a typical visual interactive model.

The purpose of this chapter is to provide a brief introduction to the simulation software that is available. First there is a description of the various types of simulation software, followed by some examples of software packages. The discussion then focuses on peripheral software, that is, packages that provide additional support to the simulation modelling process. The chapter concludes by discussing the selection of simulation software.

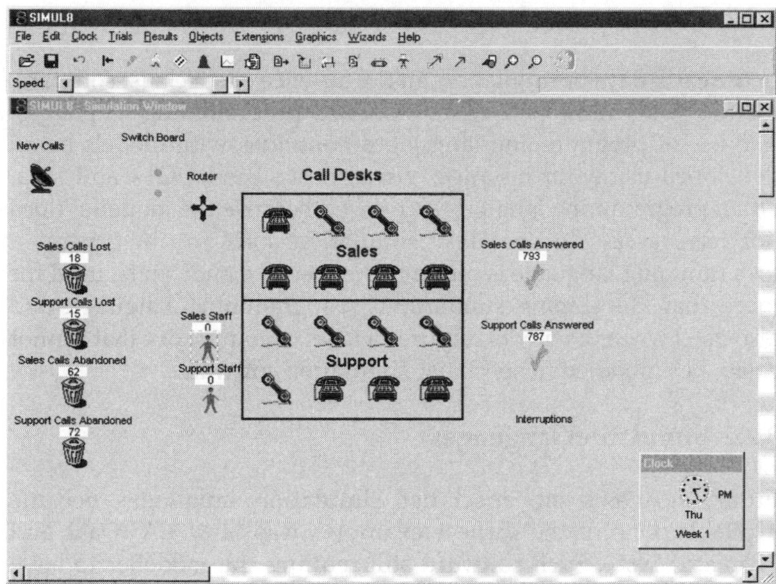

Figure 3.1 A typical VIS model of a telephone call centre

3.2 Types of simulation software

A useful way of identifying different types of simulation software is to classify them by the model building approach employed. In this respect there are three main types of simulation software (Pidd, 1998):

- Programming languages
- Simulation languages
- Visual interactive modelling systems (VIMS).

Pidd identifies a fourth type, block-structured systems, which are based upon a flow charting approach. These are not discussed here since, with the exception of the GPSS software (Schriber, 1974), this approach is now rarely used.

Simulation software can be classified in other ways, for instance, by the underlying simulation approach (for example, three-phase, activity, event or process interaction as described in Section 2.8.1). It is useful to classify the software according to the features that are of most interest to the potential user. Here it is assumed that it is the model building approach that is of most interest.

3.2.1 Programming languages

In the early days of simulation, in the absence of specialist software, models were developed using standard programming languages. The use of programming languages continues with models being developed using, for instance, Visual Basic, Pascal, C++ and Java. Often programming languages are used because the modeller does not have access to specialist simulation software; in general a programming language is much less expensive and can be used for more than developing simulations. Programming languages are also used when the model requires a level of complexity that cannot easily be embodied in specialist simulation software.

3.2.2 Simulation languages

From the 1960s on, specialist simulation languages became available. One of the earliest examples was SIMULA (Dahl and Nygaard, 1966). Such software still requires the modeller to have programming skills, similar to those required for programming languages. What they do provide, however, is a syntax that is more suited to simulation and a series of features that simplify the process of developing a simulation. Such features might include:

- A simulation executive
- Event handling and scheduling
- Animation facilities
- Collection and reporting of statistics
- Support for experimentation.

A key advantage of such specialist languages is that they reduce the time required to develop a simulation model.

3.2.3 Visual interactive modelling systems (VIMS)

With the introduction of the micro-computer in the early 1980s VIMS[1] started to appear, enabling models to be built, as well as run, in a visual and interactive manner. Models are developed by selecting from a set of pre-defined simulation objects and detailing the logic of the model through a series of menus. The model animation is also developed through a series of menus. As a result, the modeller requires little in the way of programming skills, although many VIMS either link to programming languages or have their own internal language to enable more complex logic be represented. As VIMS have been developed, more features have been added and they have become easier to use. There are now many VIMS packages on the market.

VIMS often have features that suit them to a specific purpose, for instance, manufacturing, materials handling, services or health. They range from fairly simple packages, which are limited to a few applications and low levels of complexity, to those that are able to model a wide range of applications and include quite high levels of complexity.

The main advantage of VIMS is that simulation models can be developed more quickly and easily. The main disadvantages are that they tend to be more expensive to purchase and there are limitations to the applications and complexity of models that can be built.

3.2.4 Advantages and disadvantages of alternative types of simulation software

Figure 3.2 summarizes some of the main advantages and disadvantages of programming languages, simulation languages and VIMS. In general programming languages enable a wider range of applications to be modelled and facilitate faster running models. On the other hand it is generally easier and quicker to develop models in VIMS. As a general rule VIMS are more expensive (upwards of £5000), although there are exceptions, with some costing in the same region as standard office software packages. Beware, however, as there is an extent to which the range of applications and level of complexity that can be handled by a VIMS package is reflected in its price. A simulation language can be

	Programming languages	Simulation languages	VIMS
Range of applications	Higher	——→	Lower
Ease of model development	Lower	——→	Higher
Development time	Longer	——→	Shorter
Run speed	Quicker	——→	Slower
Cost	Lower	——→	Higher

Figure 3.2 Advantages and disadvantages of alternative types of simulation software

thought of as a compromise between a programming language and a VIMS package in that it provides some of the benefits of both, while giving some of the disadvantages of both too.

3.3 Examples of simulation software

Simulation software packages are constantly being upgraded, as well as new packages appearing and some old ones disappearing! It is, therefore, fruitless to try and provide an up-to-date review of this software here. Instead, Table 3.1 provides a list of some of the simulation software that is available at the time of writing. This is not intended to be an exhaustive list with more than a hundred packages, of different shapes and sizes, having been developed world-wide.

Some useful sources of information on simulation software exist. The annual Winter Simulation Conference, held in the USA, contains specialist streams dedicated to software tutorials. The proceedings of these conferences are published, for instance, the 1998 conference (Medeiros *et al.* 1998). INFORMS (the US Institute

Table 3.1 Examples of simulation software

Simulation languages	VIMS
CSim18: Mesquite Software, Austin, Texas *Modsim III:* CACI, La Jolla, California	*Arena:* Systems Modeling, Sewickley, Pennsylvania *AutoMod:* AutoSimulations, Bountiful, Utah *Extend:* ImagineThat, San Jose, California *MicroSaint:* Micro Analysis and Design, Boulder, Colorado *ProModel:* PROMODEL, Orem, Utah *Simul8:* Simul8, Glasgow, UK *Taylor ED:* F&H Simulations, Utrecht, The Netherlands *Witness:* Lanner Group, Redditch, UK

For Operations Research and the Management Sciences) and the Institute of Industrial Engineers regularly provide directories of simulation software in their publications OR/MS Today (Swain, 1999) and IIE Solutions (Simulations Software Guide, 1998) respectively. The Society for Computer Simulation (San Diego) also provides a directory of simulation software.

3.4 Peripheral software

Other software exist that are useful for supporting the simulation modelling process. Standard spreadsheet packages are used to store simulation model data, and to analyse and report the results of simulation experiments. Specialist software can be obtained for fitting statistical distributions to empirical data, for instance, ExpertFit (Averill M. Law and Associates) and Stat::Fit (Geer Mountain Software). Meanwhile, many of the simulation software suppliers provide software for aiding simulation experimentation and analysing simulation results. In particular, so called 'optimizers' exist that search for the best combination of inputs to a model. Simulation optimization is discussed in more detail in Section 5.3.2.

3.5 Selection of simulation software

It is noted above that simulation software is expensive, and therefore, it is important that an organization purchases the package most suited to their needs. The success of a simulation study partly depends on the software that is employed (Law and McComas, 1989) although advances in computing and developments in the simulation packages that are available have served to reduce this dependence. Indeed, within a certain domain of application, there is very little to choose between the various packages. In particular, if the requirement is to build fairly standard queueing models of manufacturing or service applications, then many of the simulation packages will do a more than an adequate job.

On the other hand, models of health and warehousing applications, for instance, present greater demands on the software, and only a few of the packages have features that are suited to these purposes. Modelling complex decision processes and human factors present particular challenges, and if this is the requirement the software needs to be more carefully selected. It should be said that the problem with modelling these areas is not just the capabilities of the software, but also the ability to collect meaningful data from the real world.

As a first step in software selection it is vital that the purpose of the software is identified. Which projects is the software to be used for? The fact that there could be more than one project may lead to diverse requirements and make the selection of a single package more troublesome. Unless the software is going to be used very frequently, most organizations would not countenance the cost of purchasing more than one package, and so some compromise needs to be reached. There is often an immediate need to model a single application, and this should probably be the first consideration when selecting the software, with some cursory thought to possible future applications.

Having determined the purpose of the software, the next stage is to determine the favoured modelling approach: programming language, simulation language or VIMS. This not only depends on the purpose of the software, but also on the skills of the potential modellers. By identifying the type of simulation software required, a shortlist of potential packages can be drawn up. The next stage is then to review the shortlisted packages in some detail. A series of factors should be considered during this review, for instance:

- *Suitability for Purpose:* do the software features match the industry/application?
- *Model Development:* ease of model development, software documentation, model size limitations, input/output of data from/to external packages, model documentation facilities.
- *Sampling and Distributions:* validity of random number streams, control over random number streams, availability of statistical distributions, defining empirical distributions, distribution fitting procedures.
- *Visual Features:* ease with which the display can be developed, resolution of graphics, control over the appearance (for example, user defined icons), printing the display, 3D facilities.
- *Model Verification and Validation:* internal syntax and consistency checking, debugging aids (for example, trace).
- *Experimentation:* run-speed, facilities for setting warm-up, run-length and number of replications, facilities for automatic

running of multiple scenarios, experimental design features, availability of an 'optimizer'.
- *Reporting Features:* reports automatically provided by the software, ease of developing user reports, ability to output reports to other software, statistical analysis of reports.
- *Hardware/Software:* hardware platform required, operating system required, portability between hardware/software platforms.
- *Support:* help desk, training, consultancy support, software upgrade policy.
- *Pedigree:* size of vendor's organization, the age of the software, number of users, user's-group, similar applications, availability of literature on the software and its applications.
- *Cost:* purchase price and follow-on costs (for example, training, maintenance).

Various authors discuss the selection of simulation software, for instance, Pidd (1989, 1998), Holder (1990), Van Breedman *et al.* (1990), Banks *et al.* (1996), Hlupic (1997), Bowden (1998), Hlupic and Paul (1999) and Law and Kelton (2000). For those who are in the position of selecting a package, it is worth reading some of these articles.

References and further reading

Banks, J., Carson, J.S. and Nelson, B.L. (1996) *Discrete-Event System Simulation*, 2nd edn. Upper Saddle River, NJ: Prentice-Hall.

Bowden, R. (1998) 'The Spectrum of Simulation Software', *IIE Solutions*, May, 44–6.

Dahl, O. and Nygaard, K. (1966) 'SIMULA: An Algol-Based Simulation Language', *Communications of the ACM*, 9, 671–8.

Hlupic, V. (1997) 'Selecting Simulation Software Using SimSelect', *Simulation*, 69:4, 231–9.

Hlupic, V. and Paul, R.J. (1999) 'Guidelines for Selection of Manufacturing Simulation Software', *IIE Transactions*, 31:1, 21–9.

Holder, K. (1990) 'Selecting Simulation Software', *OR Insight*, 3:4, 19–24.

Hurrion, R.D. (1976) 'The Design, Use and Required Facilities of an Interactive Visual Computer Simulation Language to Explore Production Planning Problems'. PhD thesis, University of London.

Law, A.M. and Kelton, W.D. (2000) *Simulation Modeling and Analysis*, 3rd edn. New York: McGraw-Hill International.

Law, A.M. and McComas, M.G. (1989) 'Pitfalls to Avoid in the Simulation of Manufacturing Systems', *Industrial Engineering*, 21:5, 28–69.

Medeiros, D.J., Watson, E.F., Manivannan, M. and Carson, J. (1998) *Proceedings of the 1998 Winter Simulation Conference*, Institute of Electrical and Electronics Engineers, Piscataway, NJ.

Pidd, M. (1989. 'Choosing Discrete Simulation Software', *OR Insight*, 2:3, 22–3.

Pidd, M. (1998) *Computer Simulation in Management Science*, 4th edn. Chichester, UK: Wiley.

Schriber, T. (1974) *Simulation Using GPSS*. New York: Wiley.

SIMULATION SOFTWARE BUYER'S GUIDE (1998) *IIE Solutions*, May, 48–54.

Swain, J.J. (1999) 'Imagine New Worlds' (OR/MS Today Simulation Survey), *OR/MS Today*, February, 38–51.

Van Breedman, A., Raes, J. and Van de Velde, K. (1990) 'Segmenting the Simulation Software Market', *OR Insight*, 3:2, 9–13.

Note

1 The terms VIS and VIMS should not be confused. A VIS refers more to the way that a model is used than how it is developed. Indeed, a VIS could be developed using any of the model building approaches described here. Furthermore, a simulation model built using a VIMS may not be a VIS, since, for instance, the modeller does not always have to develop a display for the model.

Performing Simulation Studies

4.1 Introduction

There is more to simulation than simply obtaining a suitable simulation package and learning how to use it. Many pitfalls await those who do no more than learn how to type the right keys to get the software to work. This is like suggesting that someone who wants to learn to drive need only purchase a car and then be shown the appropriate controls. Assuming the learner manages to get the vehicle to move at all, the real fallacy in this suggestion becomes evident when he/she enters a busy road. At this point the fledgling driver, and anybody else who is unfortunate enough to be in the vicinity, becomes all too aware of the need to know the rules of the road and to be able to process a multiplicity of information in a short space of time while keeping the vehicle under control. There is a significant difference between knowing how to use something and being able to apply it.

It is the purpose of this chapter to move the reader from an understanding of simulation principles and the software used to develop simulation models, to an understanding of how to apply the approach to real-life problems. Therefore, the chapter outlines the requirements for the successful application of simulation, first by providing an overview of the key stages in a simulation study, and then by describing those stages in more detail.

4.2 An outline of a simulation study

Figure 4.1 shows the key stages in a simulation study. The boxes represent the stages, while the arrows represent the processes that a simulation modeller must perform to move between the stages. At the start of a simulation study there is some real world problem that needs to be tackled. This might be a shortcoming with an existing system, or a need to investigate the workings of a proposed system. Whichever, the job of the modeller is to understand what this problem is and to develop a conceptual model suitable for tackling

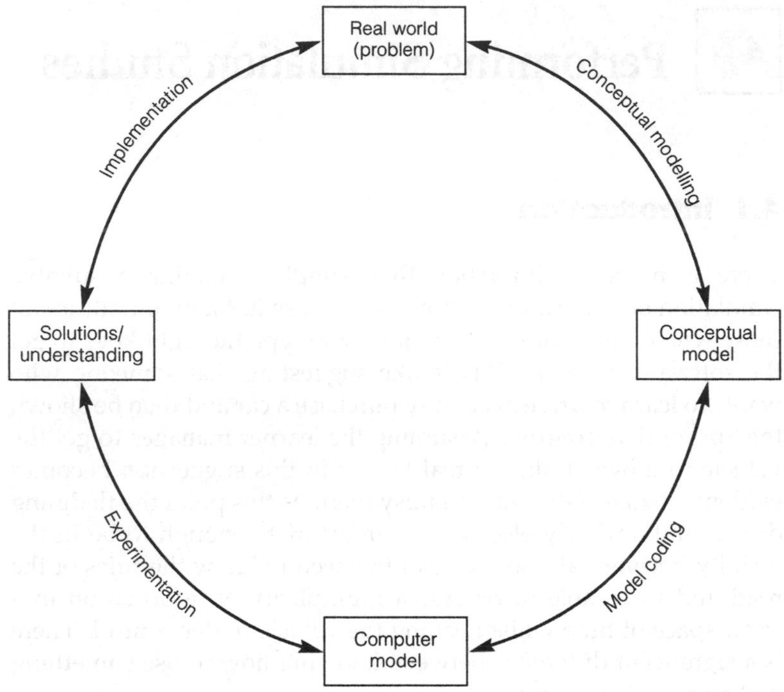

Figure 4.1 Stages in a simulation study

it. Part of this process involves the identification, collection and analysis of the data required to build the model.

Based upon the design of the conceptual model, a computer model is developed. This process, described here as model coding, normally entails the use of a specialist simulation software package (Chapter 3), though sometimes modellers opt to use a standard programming language (for example, Visual Basic, C++ or Java) or a spreadsheet (for example, Excel, possibly with Visual Basic for Applications).

The computer model is used to develop solutions to the real world problem and/or to obtain a better understanding of the real world. Because a simulation model cannot directly determine the best course of action, but simply predicts the outcome of specific policies and procedures, a great many experiments may be required to obtain a good understanding.

Once satisfactory solutions to the real world problem have been found, these can then be implemented in order to effect improvement (hopefully!) in the real world. If the modelling exercise has lead to an improved understanding of the real world, while specific courses of action may not have been identified, the improved understanding will no doubt positively affect the way that future decisions are taken.

Figure 4.1 is deliberately drawn in a circular fashion to highlight an important facet of the way in which a simulation study is performed. It is by no means a linear process, where the modeller starts by developing a full understanding of the real world problem, then develops a complete conceptual model upon which the computer model is based, and only upon completion of this model is experimentation performed. Instead, a simulation study should be seen as an iterative process of enquiry in which the modeller starts with only a partial understanding of the real world problem and gradually builds towards a fuller understanding and the development of a set of solutions. During this process the movement is not always forwards from the real world problem, to the conceptual model, to a computer model, to solutions or a better understanding. Instead, a whole series of reverse movements may be required (hence the bi-directional arrows in Figure 4.1). For instance, as the conceptual model is developed and the data required for the model are collected and analysed, so a better understanding of the real world problem is often obtained. Similarly, it may be that during experimentation an error in the model is uncovered, which necessitates a change to both the conceptual and computer model. It is also worth noting that even having completed a loop through the circle, further loops through the circle may be required to enable more detailed enquiry into the real world problem, either with the same or an alternative simulation model.

Before looking at each of the processes involved in a simulation study in more detail, the time required to perform a simulation study is considered. Obviously the time required to complete a study depends upon the scope and complexity of the project. Estimating how long a study will take before it starts is something of an art that even experienced simulation modellers get wrong. As a general guide, a study by Cochran *et al.* (1995), on the use of simulation in industrial settings, found that typical studies take between one and three months to complete. There is, however, a whole spectrum from those that take a few hours to those that take a year or more. In terms of the individual stages, a useful rule of thumb is to allow approximately a third of the time for each of conceptual modelling, model building and experimentation. Of these processes, experimentation is the one most likely to vary in length, in some cases requiring only a few comparisons, while in others many hundreds or even thousands of simulation runs may be necessary. Note that implementation is deliberately excluded from these timings since it is often performed as a separate project, in which the simulation modeller is not involved.

What is notably missing from the description of a simulation study above is any notion of the need to test the software or the model and its results; otherwise known as verification and validation. This has deliberately been excluded since it should not be seen as a stage within a simulation study, but a process that starts at the conception of the study and continues until its end. What now follows is a more detailed description of each of the processes in a simulation study, after which the verification and validation of simulations is discussed.

4.3 Conceptual modelling

The conceptual model is a software independent description of the model that is to be constructed. In other words, based upon the description of the conceptual model a computer model could be developed in any suitable simulation software (or other software). Various methods exist for representing such a model; probably the most common is the activity cycle diagram described in Section 2.3.2. In many cases, however, the conceptual model is simply a list of the elements that are to be included in a model (the scope) and the detail required for each of those elements (level of detail) including the relationships between them (for example, control rules and flow of elements).

It is necessary to put some careful thought into this stage to avoid developing models that are too simple, and so unable to tackle the problem at hand, or too complex, and so require excessive amounts of time and effort to develop. In this respect, conceptual modelling is probably the most important stage in a simulation study. The next subsection discusses the development of the conceptual model, followed by discussions on data collection and the representation of variability within simulation models.

4.3.1 Development of the conceptual model

As a first step in the conceptual modelling process it is vital that the objectives of the simulation study are determined. The objectives act as the basis for determining the content of the model (conceptual modelling), validating the model, identifying the experiments to be performed and ultimately judging the success of the project based upon whether or not the objectives have been achieved. Without objectives a simulation study lacks direction.

In general the objective should not be to develop a simulation model, since once the model is built the objective has been met without achieving any useful outcome (there are exceptions to any rule of course!). The objectives should be expressed in terms of the intended outcomes of the project. For instance, if the problem to be tackled involves the modelling of a self-service restaurant, then the objective(s) might be one or more of the following:

- To determine the number of staff required during peak operating periods.
- To determine the number of tables required in order to ensure that 95 per cent of customers are seated immediately.
- To compare alternative service area layouts to determine which minimizes waiting time.
- To provide an increased understanding of the operation of the restaurant.

Obviously, to set the objectives the modeller needs to expend a great deal of effort in understanding the background to the problem situation. Approaches such as cognitive mapping and soft systems methodology (see forthcoming books in the Palgrave Series on Operational Research) may prove useful for this purpose.

Once the objectives are determined it is possible to start considering the content of the model itself. This process is depicted in Figure 4.2. As a first step it is useful to determine the key inputs (experimental factors) and outputs (responses). The experimental factors are the data that are varied during experimentation in order to try and achieve the study's objectives. The responses are the statistics that the model provides in order to determine:

- Whether a set of values of the experimental factors does, or does not, achieve the project's objectives.
- The reasons why a set of values of the experimental factors fails to achieve the project's objectives (if they are not achieved).

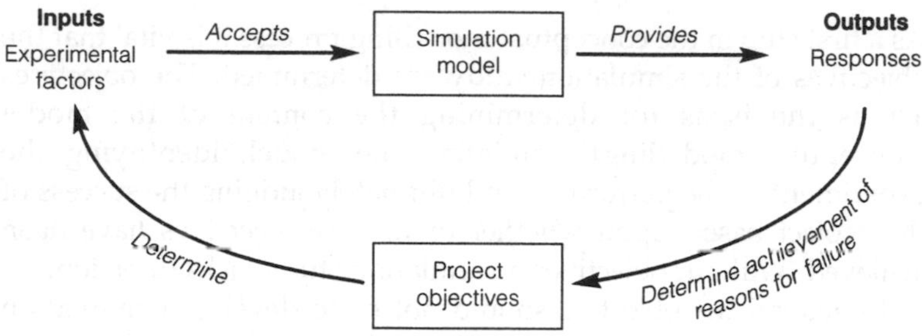

Figure 4.2 Determining the conceptual model

The latter is particularly important because it enables the identification of the reasons for failure and, therefore, possible routes to achieving the desired result. It also helps to increase the understanding of the model.

Taking the self-service restaurant example, should the objective be the second one listed above, then the experimental factors might be the number of tables of each size (2, 4, 6 seats and so on) and the positioning of the tables. Meanwhile the responses might be the percentage of customers seated immediately (has the objective been achieved?), and the waiting time of customers to be seated and the utilization of tables (why have the objectives not been achieved?).

The second step requires that the content of the model itself is determined. The simulation model needs to be capable of accepting as input the experimental factors and providing as output the necessary responses. Beyond this it is difficult to give advice on how to go about determining what to include and not include in the model. This is more an art than a science, and a skill that develops with experience. A study by Willemain (1995) of the way experts formulate OR models showed that they think about all stages of the study during the model formulation in order to imagine and estimate how well different models would perform. This is a creative process in which a variety of different models may be considered (Willemain, 1994). One recommendation, however, is to model the minimum scope and level of detail necessary to achieve the project's objectives. Indeed, there are a number of benefits in developing a simpler model (Brooks and Tobias, 1996), including:

- The model can be developed more quickly.
- The model can be more easily understood.
- The model is less likely to contain errors.
- Model validation is simpler.
- The model runs faster making more experimentation possible.

Figure 4.3 depicts the relationship between model accuracy and the scope and level of detail. What this shows is that for a relatively simple model a reasonable level of accuracy can be achieved. Adding more scope and detail beyond point X is of little advantage in terms of improving accuracy. Indeed, too much detail may eventually lead to a model that is less accurate because there simply are not sufficient data to support the detail being modelled. For instance, in the restaurant example, aiming to model why individuals choose certain tables is unlikely to provide a more accurate model because data on, or an understanding of, such behaviour is not available, although it may have some effect on the requirement for tables. It is not possible to achieve 100 per cent accuracy; models by nature are simplifications of reality.

Modellers should be aiming for approximately point X on the curve, unless there are specific reasons for having a more or less accurate model. A suggestion for determining this point is to use the approach of successive inclusion. The modeller effectively starts with a blank sheet of paper and successively adds more details until

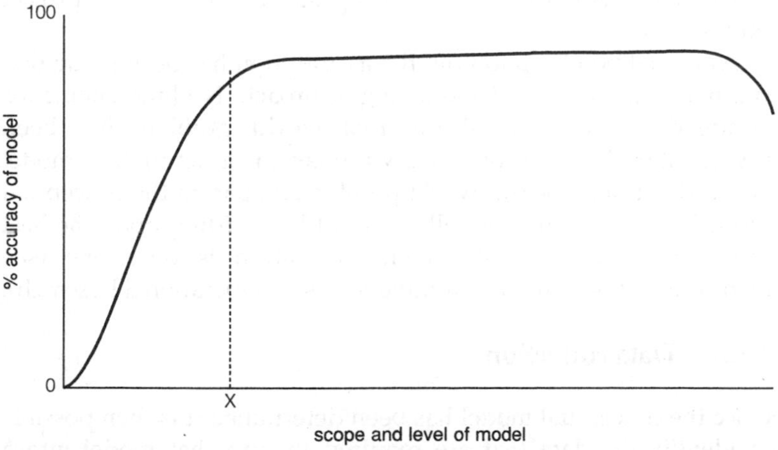

Figure 4.3 Model accuracy and scope and level of detail (Robinson, 1994a)

it is judged that an additional detail will not add significantly to the accuracy of the model. This is a process of moving from the left to the right in Figure 4.3. An alternative is to adopt a successive exclusion approach, where the modeller starts by trying to describe the complete system, and then removes detail until it is judged that the removal of further detail will significantly reduce the accuracy of the model. This is a process of moving from the right to the left in Figure 4.3.

More detailed discussions on choosing the best model and model simplification can be found in Courtois (1985) and Brooks and Tobias (1996). Robinson (1994a) describes some specific methods of simplifying simulation models.

In Section 4.2 it was noted that a simulation study is an iterative process. Therefore, it should be no surprise that the conceptual model is not static, but continuously evolving as a study proceeds. Indeed, the conceptual model needs to adapt to changes in the real world problem being tackled, for instance design changes, and to an improved understanding of the problem situation.

The conceptual model is often reflected in some form of written project specification that outlines the project's objectives, the model (experimental factors, responses, scope and level of detail), any assumptions, and the data requirements for the model (see the next subsection). The aim of the specification is to act as a means of documenting the project and for validating the approach that is being taken (Section 4.7). The specification needs to continuously reflect any changes to the conceptual model as the project progresses.

As a final point, up to now the assumption has been made that simulation is the correct modelling approach. Nothing should be assumed, however, until the real world problem has been investigated. Be wary of those who ask for a simulation model before describing the real world problem. As part of the conceptual modelling process the modeller should be deciding upon the best modelling approach, of which simulation is only one (see forthcoming books in the Palgrave Series on Operational Research).

4.3.2 Data collection

Once the conceptual model has been determined it is then possible to identify the data that are required to turn that model into a computer model (note that the conceptual modelling stage does not commence with data collection, since until the nature of the model has been determined it is not possible to predict what the data requirements are). Two types of data need to be collected: data for model building and data for model validation (Section 4.7). The data for model building, which can be identified directly from the conceptual model, include the experimental factors and the fixed data (these are the data that are necessary for the logic of the model, but for which there is no intention to try alternative values during experimentation). When developing the computer model it is often useful to separate the data from the model code by placing them in data files or a spreadsheet. This simplifies model maintenance and experimentation by providing easy access to all the data. Even data that are initially considered to be fixed may not remain so as a better understanding of the problem is gained.

Once the data requirements have been determined, the data can then be obtained. At this point the data fall into three categories (Table 4.1). The available data (category A), that is data which have already been collected, present little problem to the simulation modeller although he/she should ensure that these data are in the correct format for the simulation software that is being employed. To illustrate this, if machine breakdowns are being modelled many simulation packages ask for the 'time between failure' (TBF) to be input. There are two interpretations of this information (Figure 4.4). First, the TBF is the time from the end of the previous breakdown to the start of the next; second, the TBF is the time from the start of the previous breakdown to the start of the next. Whichever, it is important to know both how the data have been collected and how the simulation software interprets that data.

Table 4.1 Categories of data for collection

Category A:	Available
Category B:	Not available, but collectable
Category C:	Not available and not collectable

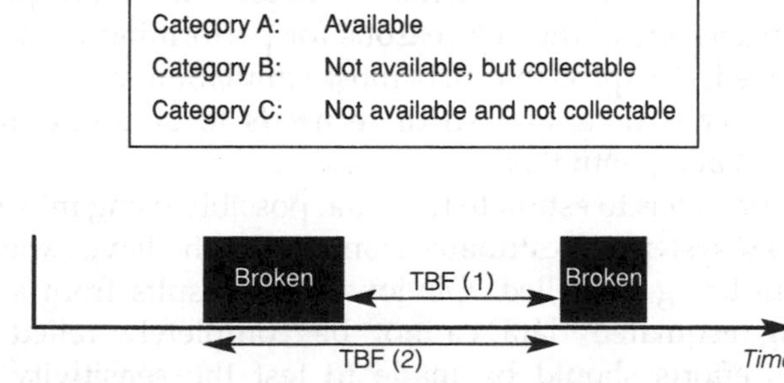

Figure 4.4 Interpretations of time between failure

It is also important not to simply accept that the data are accurate. The source of the data should be investigated with particular reference to the possibility of errors entering the information. The modeller should ascertain who collected the data, how they were collected and for what purpose. It is also useful to draw graphs (for example, scatter charts and histograms) of the data to look for any unusual patterns or outliers.

Should data fall into category B (collectable data) then careful consideration should be given to the data collection exercise. As for category A data, the information needs to be in the format required by the simulation software. Effort should be made to avoid errors in the data collection exercise. The selection of samples and the sample size must also be thoroughly considered. For instance, in modelling service systems, on which days should the data be collected, for how many days and at what times? The problem here is that the customer arrival rates vary considerably day on day, and it is likely that there is a similar effect on the rate at which customers are served; service staff tend to work faster when the queue is longer.

The time-scale of the project often determines whether data are in category B or C. If data are required on machine breakdowns, for example, and this information is not already available, it is unlikely that a satisfactory sample could be obtained within the time-scales of a typical project. For instance, a sample of four is unlikely to be sufficient to reflect the variation in machine repair times upon failure. However, if a machine breaks down on average once every week, and the time-scale of a project is only four weeks, this is all the data that are likely to be forthcoming.

Data may also be in category C simply because they cannot be collected, since the real world system is not yet in existence. After all, modelling planned systems to determine their probable performance is one of the key reasons for performing a simulation study. Indeed, it is probable that most simulation studies involve some category C data, and so there needs to be an appropriate means for dealing with them.

One approach is to estimate the data, possibly using information from similar systems or estimates from those who have expertise in the system being modelled. Obviously the results from a model containing estimated data cannot be completely relied upon. Therefore, efforts should be made to test the sensitivity of the results to the estimated data. This entails increasing and reducing the value (E) of the data by, say, 10 per cent (E+10%, E–10%), and determining the effect on the final results (Figure 4.5). If the results are insensitive to the value of the data across the range investigated, then the accuracy of the estimate, within that range, is of little importance. However, if the results prove to be sensitive, then this information should be reported, increasing the understanding of the real system, and enabling appropriate actions to be identified based upon an assessment of the risks involved.

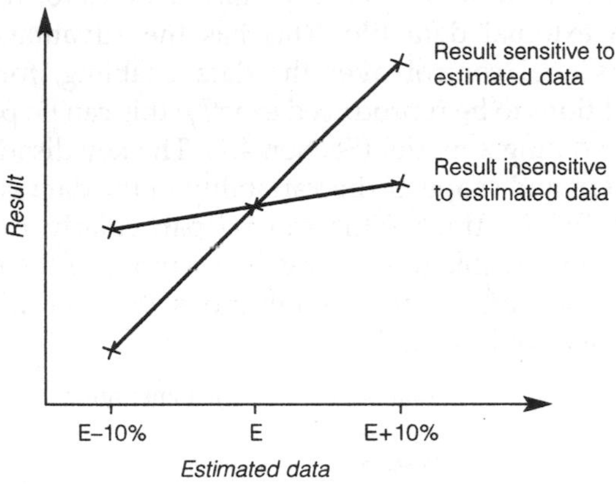

Figure 4.5 Sensitivity analysis on estimated data

An alternative means for dealing with category C data is to consider them as experimental factors rather than fixed data. The question that is being asked is: at what values for these data is the desired performance achieved? Often it is possible to have some control over data that may initially appear to be fixed. For instance, machine downtime can be reduced by regular preventative maintenance, and readily available maintenance engineers and spare parts when a machine fails.

If the data are not available, and neither of the above approaches will suffice, then the modeller needs to change the content of the model. This is reflected in a change to the conceptual model (Section 4.3.1). In this way the requirement for the category C data can be removed. This may mean, of course, that some of the project's objectives cannot be achieved, or at least not to the level of accuracy originally desired.

4.3.3 Representing variability

One of the key benefits of the simulation approach is its ability to model unpredictable events and their interactions (Section 2.4). There are three approaches to representing such variability in simulation models: traces (or data streams), empirical distributions and statistical distributions. A trace is a stream of data, for instance customer arrival times (Table 4.2), that is read directly into the simulation model in order to generate events at the time specified in the data. Most simulation software has facilities for reading in a trace via an external data file. This has the advantage that the modeller has total control over the data enabling, for example, historic conditions to be reproduced exactly; this can be particularly useful for validating a model (Section 4.7). The key disadvantage is that the pattern and scope of the variability in the data is limited to that defined by the trace. This can be particularly troublesome because it is not possible to increase the accuracy of the simulation result by performing multiple replications (Section 4.5.1) unless more than one trace is available.

Table 4.2 Example of a trace (data stream) for customer arrivals

Customer	*Arrival time (mins)*
1	3.21
2	5.48
3	11.91
4	12.80
5	15.36
...	...

Empirical distributions provide a second means for representing variability. An example, for customer inter-arrival times, is shown in Figure 4.6. Note that inter-arrival times (for example, minutes between customers), rather than arrival rates (for example, customers per minute), are normally used in simulations to depict the time between successive events. The means by which random numbers can be used to generate samples from empirical distributions is discussed in Section 2.4. Meanwhile, simulation software packages have facilities for defining empirical distributions and for generating random numbers and sampling from such distributions. The two main advantages of this approach are that: different patterns of variability can be generated by using different streams of random numbers, enabling multiple replications to be performed (Section 4.5.1); any shape of distribution can be represented. The key disadvantage is that the data in the distribution are only a sample and so are not totally representative of the true population. The sample may contain irregularities and may be limited in the scope of its variation.

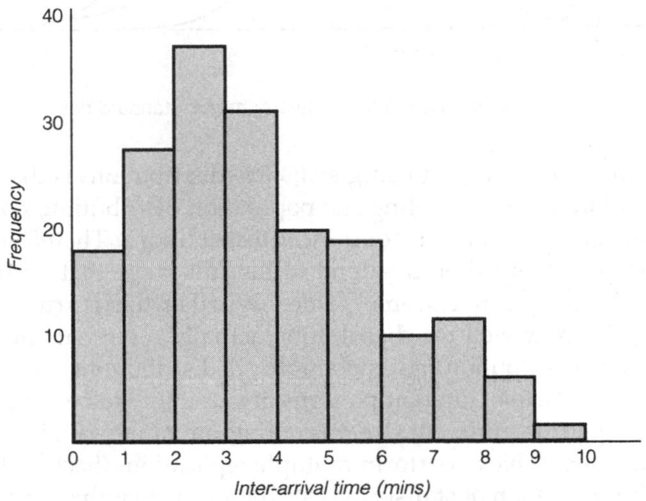

Figure 4.6 Example of an empirical distribution for customer arrivals

The third approach to representing variability is to use a statistical distribution. Probably the best known of these is the normal distribution (Figure 4.7), although it is not commonly employed in simulation models. With a continuous distribution, such as the normal, the equivalent to the histogram of Figure 4.6 is the probability density function (pdf). Like a histogram, the area under the pdf curve within a given range gives the probability of obtaining a value in that range. So, for the normal distribution the most probable occurrence is to obtain a value close to the mean, with very low probabilities of the values in the left and right tails. Simulation software packages have facilities for generating samples from statistical distributions (for a detailed discussion see Pidd, 1998), the modeller need only specify the distribution and its parameters (for example, for the normal distribution this is the mean and the standard deviation).

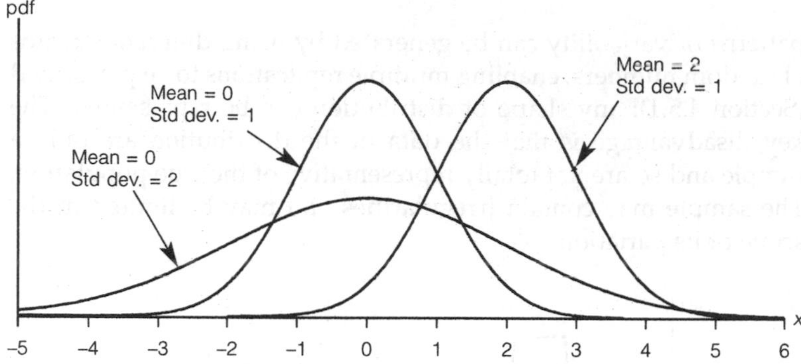

Figure 4.7 The normal distribution (parameters: mean, standard deviation)

The main advantage of using statistical distributions is that they are an attempt at representing the population distribution, not just a sample, as is the case for empirical distributions. Therefore, the scope of variability should extend to the full range that occurs in reality, including rare extreme values. Whether this is true or not depends on how well the distribution actually represents the true population distribution. As for empirical distributions, statistical distributions enable different patterns of variability to be generated by sampling from different streams of random numbers, giving the benefit of being able to perform multiple replications (Section 4.5.1). The main limitation of statistical distributions is that there may not be a distribution that adequately describes the shape of the data, for instance, if there is more than one peak in the data.

The normal distribution is typically used to represent the variation of some physical attribute (for example, length or weight), and so lends itself to models involving elements of quality control. A difficulty with the normal distribution is there is no limit to the range of values that can be sampled, albeit that the probability of extremes is very low. In particular, it is possible to obtain negative values. As a result, it is sometimes necessary to ignore extreme values and to re-sample; this is referred to as a 'truncated' normal distribution.

A distribution that is far more commonly used in simulation modelling is the negative exponential distribution (Figure 4.8), sometimes referred to simply as the exponential distribution. Those that have studied queueing theory (see other books in the Palgrave Series on Operational Research) will be familiar with this distribution. It is used for representing inter-arrival times (for

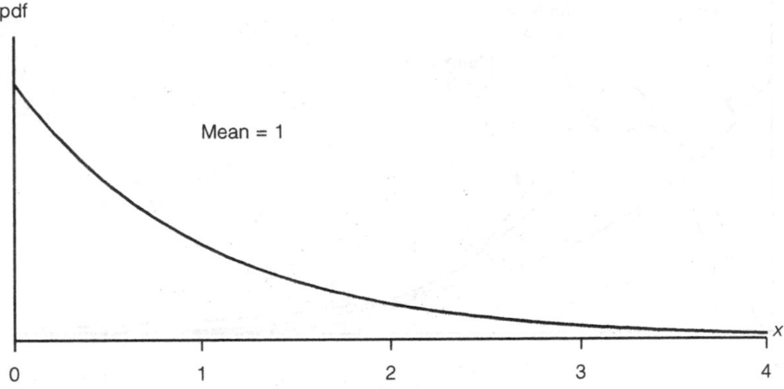

Figure 4.8 The negative exponential distribution (parameter: mean)

example, customer inter-arrivals and time between failure of machines) and is derived from studies of purely random arrival processes. What it provides is a high probability of small inter-arrival times with occasional long gaps between arrivals. A great advantage of the negative exponential distribution is that the only parameter is the mean of the distribution. Also, the assumption of random arrivals, on which it is based, is often reasonable in real situations.

The negative exponential distribution is also used for representing service times, such as customer service or machine repair times. In this context, however, it suffers from the limitation that very small values are quite common, which is usually unrealistic.

The Erlang distribution (Figure 4.9) has two parameters, the mean and a positive integer value K that determines the shape of the distribution. If K is 1 the Erlang distribution is equivalent to the negative exponential distribution. The Erlang distribution is always positively skewed (long tail to the right) but as the value of K increases the skew reduces. The Erlang distribution is often used for service times with typical values of K being between 2 and 5. It is also used with these K values for inter-arrival times, and can be particularly useful when arrivals cannot occur simultaneously, for instance, ships arriving in a harbour.

Two distributions that may be useful in the absence of any detailed data are the triangular and uniform distributions (Figures

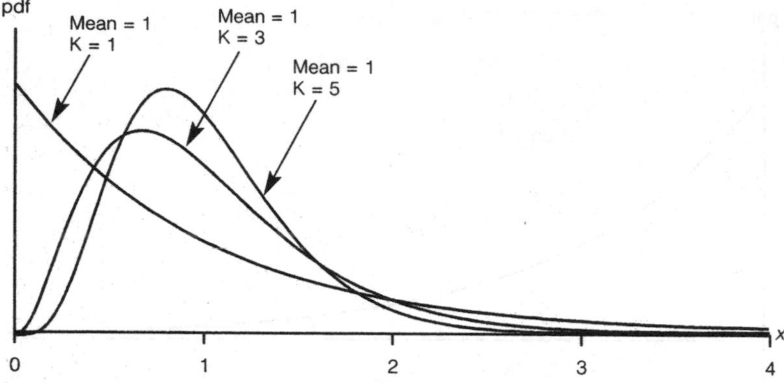

Figure 4.9 The Erlang distribution (parameters: mean, K)

4.10 and 4.11 respectively). These could be used for representing estimated category C data (Section 4.3.2). If estimates can be obtained of the minimum, mode (most likely) and maximum values of the data, then the triangular distribution may provide a useful approximation. If only the minimum and maximum can be estimated, the uniform distribution can be used.

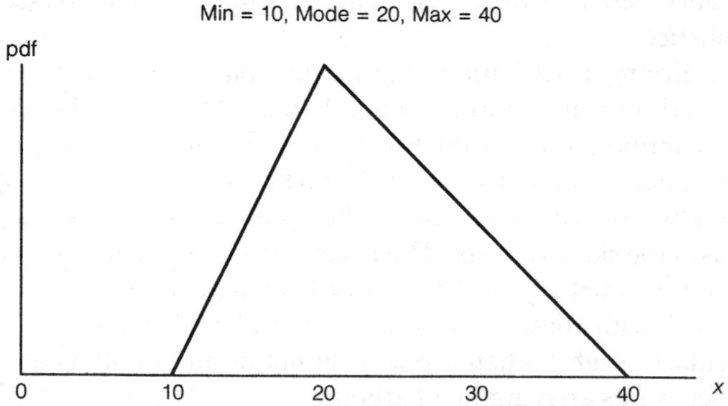

Figure 4.10 The triangular distribution (parameters: minimum, mode, maximum)

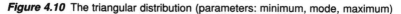

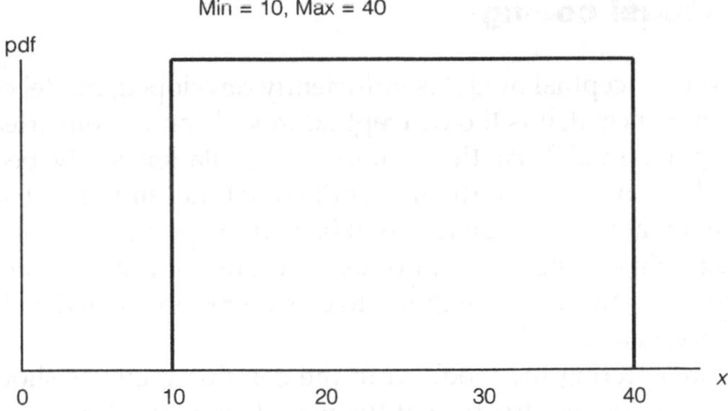

Figure 4.11 The uniform distribution (parameters: minimum, maximum)

Many other statistical distributions exist that can prove useful for simulation modelling. Among these are the beta, binomial, gamma, log normal, Poisson and Weibull distributions. For a description of these distributions and their use see Robinson (1994a), Banks *et al.* (1996) or Law and Kelton (2000).

The question that arises is: how can a modeller determine which is the correct statistical distribution in a specific circumstance? Where little more is known about the characteristic than the key statistics, for instance, mean inter-arrival time, then this decision should be based on the known facets of the distributions. So typically, a negative exponential distribution would be used for inter-arrival times and an Erlang distribution for service times, although an educated guess would be required for the K parameter.

Alternatively, if a sample of empirical data exists, then the fit of a statistical distribution can be tested using a variety of heuristic and statistical techniques. Indeed, bearing in mind the advantages of statistical distributions, the general recommendation is that they should be fitted whenever possible. Among the techniques available are frequency comparisons, Q-Q plots, P-P plots, the chi-square test and the Kolmogorov-Smirnov test. For a detailed description of these tests see Banks *et al.* (1996) and Law and Kelton (2000). Alternatively, a number of curve fitting packages are available that automatically perform these tests and identify the best fitting distributions.

4.4 Model coding

Once the conceptual model is sufficiently developed, model coding can commence, that is the conceptual model can be converted into a computer model. At this point the simulation study becomes dependent on specific software for the first time; although it should be noted that many modellers will be tied to specific software from the beginning of the project, not least because of previous software investments, and will take this into consideration when developing the conceptual model.

Before entering the model into the computer, efforts should be made to design the structure of the model, on paper, for the specific software that is to be used. This normally requires that the details of the conceptual model are converted into the building blocks (for example, elements, entities, sets, objects) of the simulation software. At this point, consideration should be given to the best methods of representing the logic of the model. Designing the model on paper first can save time by making sure that the structure is properly thought through. It also provides a basis for model documentation.

Model coding is performed best in small iterative steps, developing a portion of the model, documenting that portion and testing (verifying and validating) it. Many simulation software packages support this approach by providing facilities for interactive model coding and the running of partially completed models. It is recommended that the models are both documented and tested throughout model coding, since these tasks are unlikely to be performed satisfactorily if they are left until model coding is complete. By this point the modeller is unlikely to remember all the detail of the model and time pressures will no doubt divert attention towards completing the project. Verification and validation is discussed in more detail in Section 4.7.

4.5 Experimentation

In performing simulation experiments there are two distinct decisions to be made. First, how can sufficiently accurate results be obtained from the model? Second, if there are many different options, which scenarios should be experimented with? What now follows is a discussion on these issues which provides some pointers to how these questions can be answered. The section then concludes with a discussion on the analysis of the results obtained from the simulation experiments.

4.5.1 Obtaining sufficiently accurate results

Obviously, the accuracy of the results largely depends on the accuracy of the model and the data that are input to it. These issues are discussed in the section on conceptual modelling (Section 4.3) and verification and validation (Section 4.7). Here the concern is with how the experimentation with that model affects the accuracy of the results obtained.

The output from a simulation model typically looks like the time-series in Figure 4.12. This shows an initial period in which the values are low but there is an upward trend, followed by a series of observations that vary around some fixed mean. For instance, when a simulation of a manufacturing facility starts running there is normally no work-in-progress in the model. Therefore, there is no throughput for the initial time-periods. After this the throughput climbs to its 'normal' level. The throughput is not steady, however, but varies due to breakdowns, changeovers and such like; those aspects which are modelled as random events. The first period is known as the 'initial transient' after which the model reaches a 'steady-state'. This does not imply that the output ceases to vary, but that it varies according to some fixed distribution with a fixed mean.

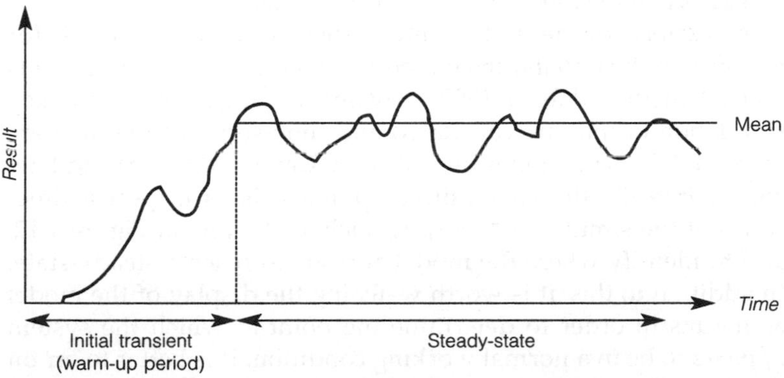

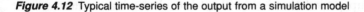

Figure 4.12 Typical time-series of the output from a simulation model

Many business simulation models display steady-state behaviour, therefore, the discussion that follows focuses on these types of models and their analysis. There is a brief discussion at the end of this section on alternative output behaviours.

A run of a simulation model basically provides a sample of data (results) about the performance of the system being modelled. It is the modellers task to infer information about the overall (population) performance of the system from these data. In order to do this, the modeller must ensure that there is no bias in the data and that the sample is sufficiently large to make satisfactory inferences. It is these two issues that are now discussed.

Removing bias from the simulation results

Should the initial transient period be included in the analysis of the simulation results then this will introduce some bias by providing an estimate of mean performance that is too low. Therefore, the modeller's task is to ensure that the initial transient period is excluded from the results by running the model for a 'warm-up' period before starting to collect any statistics. For example, the output statistic of interest might be the mean steady-state throughput. To calculate this automatically for each run, the simulation must only record the total throughput that occurs within the steady-state period. To enable this, the modeller must specify the length of the warm-up period based on an analysis of some preliminary simulation runs. In these runs, he/she must be able to identify when the initial transient period ends, or, in other words, when the model reaches steady-state.

A variety of heuristic and statistical methods exist for identifying the initial transient period. One of the most popular is Welch's method (Welch, 1983) in which moving averages of a key simulation output are calculated and time-series of the data are inspected. This method is described in Robinson (1994a) and Law and Kelton (2000). An intuitive approach is to inspect a time-series of the simulation's output, such as the one in Figure 4.12, and to identify where the model appears to reach a steady-state. In addition to this, it is worth watching the display of the model as it runs in order to determine the point at which the system appears to be in a normal working condition. It is better to err on the side of caution and use a longer warm-up when doing this. A warm-up period that is too short introduces bias, whereas one that is longer than necessary just extends the length of the simulation runs.

For some models a warm-up period is unnecessary. This is particularly true of simulations of service systems that often start the day with no customers in the system. If, however, the intention is to model the busiest period of the day, then the assumption that the system is empty at, say, the beginning of the lunch period is incorrect, and some warm-up is required.

Most simulation software has an option to specify the warm-up period. On running the model, all the results are reset at the end of the warm-up period and so the final results only take into account the events that follow.

Determining the sample

As with any sampling exercise, the accuracy of the estimates can be improved by increasing the sample size and taking more samples. In simulation terms this means running the models for longer and performing 'multiple replications' respectively.

For some models the run-length is determined by some natural end point. For instance, a model that aims to test a one-month production schedule has a natural end point at the end of the month. Many models of service systems are only run for one day, since the system starts and finishes each day in the same state, that is, with no customers. Such models are known as 'terminating'. For other models, however, there is no natural end point, and the simulation can be run until the modeller decides to interrupt it. These models are known as 'non-terminating'. Many manufacturing models built to aid facilities design fall into this category, for example, a model of an engine assembly line. The run-length for these models is often determined by some identifiable period, for example, one year, or by the practicalities of how much time is available to perform a simulation run. The run-length may be limited by how far the simulation can be run overnight. One method for aiding the selection of a suitable run-length for a non-terminating simulation is described in Robinson (1995). This is based on the comparison of time-series of the cumulative average of a key output statistic over a series of simulation runs.

For terminating simulations, because the size of the sample is restricted, the only means available for improving the accuracy of the results is to take more samples. This can be done by performing 'multiple replications'. A replication is a simulation run that utilizes specific streams of random numbers. By changing the streams of random numbers a different sequence of random events will take place, and so a different result will be obtained. This result is effectively a different sample from the same population distribution. Multiple replications, therefore, are a series of simulation runs, with the same model, that utilize different streams of random numbers. Most simulation software packages provide facilities for random number control (selecting which streams of random numbers to use) and for automatic running of multiple replications.

Table 4.3 Results from five replications with a simulation model of a service queue

Replication	*Average waiting time (mins)*
1	2.34
2	1.86
3	2.57
4	2.03
5	1.92
Mean	2.14

As an illustration, Table 4.3 shows a series of results obtained from five replications with a simulation model of a queue in a service system. The estimate of the system's performance is provided by calculating the mean across the five replications. It is notable that there is some variation between these results, and had only the first replication been performed, the performance of the system (2.34 mins) would have appeared worse than that estimated by the five replications (2.14 mins).

The analysis can be extended by calculating a 'confidence interval' for the five replications. A confidence interval is a means for expressing the accuracy of an estimate, by stating in what range the true mean is expected to fall based on the samples obtained. The theory behind confidence intervals is not discussed here, but can be found in any elementary statistics book. Indeed, the construction of confidence intervals for simulation model results can be found in many simulation texts, for instance, Robinson (1994a), Banks *et al.* (1996) and Law and Kelton (2000).

The interval can be calculated using the following formula:

$$\text{Confidence interval} = \text{Mean} \pm t_{n-1,\,\alpha/2} \frac{\text{Standard deviation}}{\sqrt{n}} \qquad (4.1)$$

where

n = number of replications

$t_{n-1,\,\alpha/2}$ = value from students t–distribution with n–1 degrees of freedom and significance level $\alpha/2$.

The standard deviation can be calculated by:

$$\text{Standard deviation} = \sqrt{\frac{\sum_{i=1}^{n} (\text{Result}_i - \text{Mean})^2}{n-1}} \qquad (4.2)$$

The significance level α describes the degree of confidence that is required from the interval. A typical value is 5 per cent, meaning that there is 95 per cent (100–5%) confidence that the true mean falls within the confidence interval. If a higher degree of confidence is required then a smaller value for the significance level can be used, at the sacrifice, however, of obtaining a wider confidence interval. In other words, the wider the interval the more confidence there is that the true mean falls within that range. Values for the student's t-distribution can be found in most statistics books.

The calculation of a confidence interval for the results in Table 4.3 is shown in Table 4.4. What this shows is that based on the results obtained there is 95 per cent confidence that the true mean waiting time is between 1.77 mins and 2.51 mins (2.14 ± 0.37). This interval seems quite wide and may be too wide to be useful. It can, however, be made narrower by performing more replications and so increasing the number of samples included in the confidence interval calculation.

Although it is stated above that multiple replications are used for improving the accuracy of the results from terminating simulations, they can also be used for non-terminating simulations. Indeed, without performing multiple replications it is not easy to construct a confidence interval because the data are not independent of each other (Law and Kelton, 2000).

Table 4.4 Calculation of a confidence interval for the results in Table 4.3

Replication	*Result*	*(Result–Mean)^2*
1	2.34	0.0400
2	1.86	0.0784
3	2.57	0.1849
4	2.03	0.0121
5	1.92	0.0484
Total	10.72	0.3638

$$\text{Mean} = \frac{10.72}{5} = 2.14$$

$$\text{Standard deviation} = \sqrt{\frac{0.3638}{5-1}} = 0.3016$$

$$\alpha = 5\%$$
$$t_{4,\,0.025} = 2.776$$
$$\text{Confidence interval} = 2.14 \pm 2.776\,\frac{0.3016}{\sqrt{5}}$$

$$\text{Confidence interval} = 2.14 \pm 0.37$$

The question arises: how many replications should be performed with a model? The simple answer is at least three to five (Law and Kelton, 2000). This answer, however, does not take into account the characteristics of the model that is being experimented with. A common approach is to keep performing more replications until a confidence interval that is sufficiently narrow is obtained. This may mean that only three or four replications are required, but on the other hand 20 or 30 may be necessary. The general rule is that the more a model can be run the better. Performing longer runs (for non-terminating simulations) and performing more replications can only improve the accuracy of the estimates obtained.

Alternative output behaviours

The discussion above focuses on steady-state output from simulation models. Simulations do, however, display other types of output characteristics. Some models never reach steady-state but remain transient, for example, a model of customers boarding an aeroplane showing the time from when passengers start to enter the plane until the point at which all passengers are seated. For these models the concepts of warm-up and steady-state are not relevant. The analysis of such simulations should take account of the whole period of the simulation.

Other models shift from one steady-state to another, only achieving temporary periods in any state. Such behaviour, discussed by Robinson *et al.* (1999), is little understood and is often considered to be purely transient, although some benefits may be gained by identifying the periods of steady-state in the output.

4.5.2 Planning experimental scenarios

Simulation experiments are performed in two basic modes: the first requires that a limited number of options are compared (for example, buy one machine or two); the second, that some target or optimum is sought by changing the values of the experimental factors. For the first case the selection of experimental scenarios is trivial, especially as it is highly likely that simulation runs can be performed for all the options in the time available. Careful planning is required, however, where some target or optimum is sought.

Take, for example, a model which has five experimental factors (for instance, one might be service time) all of which can be set to five different values (such as, expected, expected ±5 per cent, expected ±10 per cent). In total there would be 5^5 (3125) experimental scenarios. If five replications are required for each scenario, then a total of 15625 simulation runs would be needed. Even if a simulation run takes just five minutes to perform (a very conservative estimate for a model of any size), all the experiments would take about 54 days to complete, and that excludes the time to set-up the experiments and analyse the results. Obviously some means is required to reduce the number of experiments that need to be performed.

One approach is for the modeller to carry out some up-front data analysis in an attempt to predict the combinations of experimental factors that are likely to yield the desired result. Performing exploratory runs can also prove useful, helping the modeller to learn about the behaviour of the system and further identify promising combinations of experimental factors.

Beyond this, more formal approaches need to be used. Methods of experimental design have been developed for just these types of circumstances. Experimental runs are performed for a limited number of scenarios and the results used to predict the results of the model under scenarios for which simulation runs have not been performed. Introductions to these methods, which are beyond the scope of this chapter, can be found in Banks *et al.* (1996) and Law and Kelton (2000).

Until recently simulation software packages have offered little help with experimental design. However, in recent years many of the software vendors have offered an 'optimizer' with their software. These automate the process of searching for an optimum or a target, although an optimum cannot be guaranteed. Simulation optimization is discussed in more detail in Section 5.3.2.

4.5.3 Analysis and reporting of results

Having obtained the results from a set of experiments, it is important that they are appropriately analysed. At the centre of this are the methods described in Section 4.5.1. Simulation output analysis is a vast subject to which books and streams at conferences are devoted. Useful introductions can be found in Welch (1983), Banks *et al.* (1996) and Law and Kelton (2000).

The main purpose of analysing the results is to check the extent to which the objectives of the simulation study have been achieved. It is particularly important to remember that the results are only estimates of the real system's performance. Confidence intervals (see equation 4.1 in Section 4.5.1) should be used to give some indication of the range within which the real system's performance is likely to lie. Consideration should also be given to the variability in the results. By how much is the system's performance likely to vary on, say, a day to day basis? One of the main benefits of simulation is being able to predict not only the average performance of a system but also the variability. Measures such as the maximum, minimum and standard deviation are useful for this purpose, along with histograms and time-series showing the variability in the results. Time should be devoted to observing the behaviour of the model as it runs. This can be particularly beneficial in providing a better understanding of the real life system.

It is also useful to perform some sensitivity analysis, similar to that described in Section 4.3.2, to test the robustness of the findings from the model. This should not just entail an investigation into the sensitivity of the results to the accuracy of the estimated (category C) data. Other data should be varied, particularly those that might be open to change in the future, in order to determine the effect on the results. This can provide useful information and guide a decision-maker towards solutions that are more robust.

Once the results are analysed, the findings need to be communicated to the clients for whom the work has been performed, normally in a written report. Such a report should outline the project's objectives, provide a summary of the model and the experiments performed, detail the validation of the model, and describe the key results, conclusions and recommendations arising from the project. Opportunity should also be taken to identify any areas for further work.

4.6 Implementation

Upon reporting the results of the simulation study, the hope is that the clients will want to implement the findings. This depends in part on the confidence that the clients have in the work that has been performed, which in turn depends not only on the technical content of the work, but on the way in which the work has been delivered. This chapter largely focuses on the technical aspects of a simulation study. There is, however, a need to carefully manage the relationship with the clients and their expectations of the simulation study (Robinson and Pidd, 1998). Whether the results are implemented or not also depends on factors outside the modeller's control, for instance, whether sufficient finance is available.

Assuming that implementation does go ahead, the modeller may or may not be involved. If the modeller is an external consultant then it is unlikely that his/her involvement will extend beyond the end of the simulation work. Even for those working inside an organization, their services may be dispensed with once the simulation results are made public, freeing them to move onto other projects within the organization.

Whether the modeller is involved in the implementation or not, this process is to a large extent a separate project from the simulation study itself. It may, indeed, be a project that takes a number of months or even years to complete. The simulation model may not be put into complete retirement, however, and probably it should not. The model can act as a plan against which the implementation can be compared. Also, the real world continues to change and so new issues arise that may affect the conclusions of the original simulation work. These changes and issues could be explored in the simulation model. This emphasizes again the iterative nature of a simulation study.

Discussions on the implementation of simulation results can be found in Hoover and Perry (1990) and Robinson (1994a), with general discussions on implementation in Operational Research in Ackoff and Sasieni (1968) and Schultz and Slevin (1975), and a brief introduction in Pidd (1991).

4.7 Verification and validation

The outline of a simulation study in Section 4.2 described nothing of the need to test the model and its results. This is because the process of verification and validation should not been seen as a stage within a simulation study, but as a process that continues throughout the project. This section describes the various forms of verification and validation that should take place during a simulation study.

Verification is the process of ensuring that the conceptual model has been transformed into a computer model with sufficient accuracy; building the model right. Validation is the process of ensuring that the model is sufficiently accurate for the purpose at hand; building the right model. No model is ever 100 per cent accurate, and need only be sufficiently accurate to answer the questions that are asked of it (this same concept is discussed in Section 4.3.1 on conceptual modelling). Therefore, all validation is carried out with respect to the project's objectives. A model that is purely for demonstration purposes would in general need to be less accurate than a model of the same system that is to be used for layout planning. This in turn would need to be less accurate than a model that is to be used for real-time control of the same system.

The requirements for verification and validation can be better understood by mapping them onto the process of performing a simulation study. Figure 4.13 does this by adding various verification and validation activities to the outline of a simulation study that is shown in Figure 4.1. What this shows is that each process in a simulation study is matched by a requirement to test

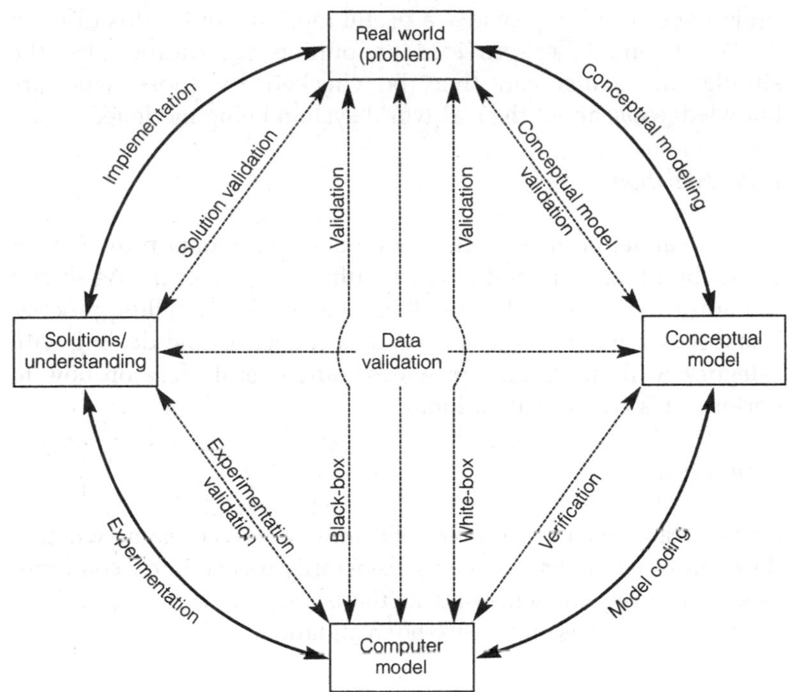

Figure 4.13 Simulation model verification and validation in the process of a simulation study (Robinson, 1999)

how well that process has been performed. Consequently the conceptual model is tested through conceptual model validation; the model coding is tested via verification; the experimentation is tested through experimentation validation; and the implementation via solution validation. Above and beyond this testing are some more general validation requirements: white-box validation, black-box validation and data validation. All of these are described below, with some comments on how they might be performed.

Conceptual model validation

The aim of conceptual model validation is to determine whether the scope and level of detail of the proposed model is sufficient for the purpose at hand, and that any assumptions are correct. There are no formal methods for conceptual model validation, although the project specification provides a useful mechanism for this (Section 4.3.1). The modeller provides an outline specification for the simulation, which can then be checked by those who are knowledgeable about the real world system being modelled.

Data validation

In data validation it is determined whether the data provided for model building and validation are sufficiently accurate. As shown in Figure 4.13, this applies to all aspects of the modelling process. The discussion in Section 4.3.2 on data collection and dealing with category A, B and C data provides some useful ideas on how to perform this type of validation.

Verification

It has already been stated that verification involves testing whether the conceptual model has been satisfactorily turned into a computer model. The requirements and methods for verifying a model are very similar to those for white-box validation.

White-box validation

The purpose of white-box validation is to determine whether the constituent parts of the computer model represent the corresponding real world elements with sufficient accuracy. This is a detailed, or micro, check of the model. In this respect white-box validation and verification are very similar, except that in verification the computer model is compared to the conceptual model, while in white-box validation, the computer model is compared to the real world. Suppose, for instance, that it has been defined in the conceptual model that a specific operator performs a task in two minutes. When coding the simulation, the modeller should first check that when the model runs the operator takes two minutes to perform the task (verification), but the modeller should also show the model to those who are knowledgeable about the system being modelled and obtain their confirmation that this aspect of the model is working in a similar way to the real system (white-box validation).

Both verification and white-box validation are performed throughout model coding. The model should be built in small steps, at each stage verifying it against the conceptual model specification. Opportunity should also be taken to regularly demonstrate the model to those knowledgeable about the real world system in order to white-box validate it.

All aspects of the model should be verified and white-box validated, including timings, the control of the elements, the control of flows, control logic and sampling from distributions. This can be done by:

- *Checking the code:* has the right information been typed into the computer?
- *Visual checks:* does the model animation suggest that the model behaves correctly?
- *Inspection of results:* do the results match the expectations of the behaviour of each element in the model?

Black-box validation

In black-box validation it is determined whether the overall model represents the real world with sufficient accuracy. This is an overall, or macro, check of the model's operation. The modeller is not concerned here with the internal workings of the model (hence the term black-box), but only with the output from the model.

Black-box validation is often performed by comparing the output from the model with that of the real system to determine whether they are sufficiently similar. This requires that data are available on the performance of the real system. In many cases such data do not exist, especially if the real system is only in the planning stage. In such cases, the simulation can be compared against other, simpler, models. For instance, a useful approach is to take all the variability out of the simulation. Then it is normally possible to predict exactly the results of the simulation. Another approach is to leave the variability in the simulation and to perform some calculations in order to determine approximately how the simulation will perform. Queueing theory may prove to be of some use for such validation (see forthcoming books in the Palgrave Series on Operational Research). Although these simplified models do not provide an exact result (if they did the simulation would not be required!), they do provide an indication of how the simulation is expected to perform. Any large deviations from this expectation may indicate that there is a problem with the simulation model.

Experimentation validation

The aim of experimentation validation is to determine whether the experimental procedures adopted are providing results that are sufficiently accurate. Key issues are the requirements for warm-up, run-length, replications, experimental design and sensitivity analysis to assure the accuracy of the results. These issues are discussed in Section 4.5.

Solution validation

Solution validation entails a determination of whether the results obtained from the model of the proposed solution are sufficiently accurate. This is similar to black-box validation in that it entails a comparison with the real world. It is different in that it only compares the final model of the proposed solution to the implemented solution. Consequently, solution validation can only take place post-implementation and so, unlike the other forms of validation, it is not intrinsic to the simulation study itself.

In practice solution validation rarely takes place, because learning whether the solution was accurate once it has been implemented is of limited interest. Little is to be gained at this point (except for some satisfaction, or not, on behalf of the modeller) because it is too late to change the solution. Another difficulty occurs if the simulation has been used purely for improving understanding. It is very difficult to measure an improved understanding!

The discussion above gives only brief details on how to go about performing verification and validation during a simulation study. More detailed discussions can be found in Sargent (1982), Balci (1994a, 1994b), Kleijnen (1995) and Robinson (1999).

Before leaving the subject of verification and validation, a word of warning. It is not possible ever to say that a model is valid, because it is not possible to test every aspect of a model. In particular, problems exist because:

- There are insufficient accurate real world data for comparison purposes;
- Most simulations are models of proposed systems (that is, a change to an existing system or a completely new system), not currently existing ones, making comparison impossible;

- There is simply insufficient time to verify and validate all aspects of a model.

As a consequence, simulation validation should not be seen as a process of validation, but one of invalidation. In other words, a validation test is not performed to try and prove that the model is valid, but that it is invalid. If it cannot be proved that the model is invalid, then that increases the confidence that the model may be valid. The more tests that can be performed in which the model cannot be shown to be invalid, the more confidence in the model grows. However, it is always possible that the next validation test will find that there is an error in the model. Therefore, when performing simulation verification and validation as many tests as possible should be performed in order to increase as far as possible the confidence that can be placed in the model.

4.8 Conclusion

This chapter describes the key stages in a simulation study and the processes that interlink these stages. It is shown that a simulation study is not a linear process but an iterative one, moving from the original definition of the problem to some solution to, or improved understanding of, that problem. Implicit to the simulation study is the need to verify and validate the model during each process and at every stage. The description here provides only an overview of the requirements and methods that can be used for each process. Where appropriate, references are made to books and papers that provide a useful starting point for further investigation into these issues.

References and further reading

Ackoff, R.L. and Sasieni, M. (1968) *Fundamentals of Operations Research*. Chichester, UK: Wiley.

Balci, O. (1985) 'Guidelines for Successful Simulation Studies', Technical Report TR-85-2, Department of Computer Science, Virginia Tech., Blacksburg, VA.

Balci, O. (1994a) 'Principles of Simulation Model Validation, Verification, and Testing', Department of Computer Science, Virginia Tech., Blacksburg, VA.

Balci, O. (1994b) 'Validation, Verification, and Testing Techniques Throughout the Life Cycle of a Simulation Study', *Annals of Operations Research*, 53, 121–73.

Banks, J., Carson, J.S. and Nelson, B.L. (1996) *Discrete-Event System Simulation*, 2nd edn. Upper Saddle River, NJ: Prentice-Hall.

Brooks, R.J. and Tobias, A.M. (1996) 'Choosing the Best Model: Level of Detail, Complexity and Model Performance', *Mathematical and Computer Modelling*, 24:4, 1–14.

Cochran, J.K., Mackulak, G.T. and Savory, P.A. (1995) 'Simulation Project Characteristics in Industrial Settings', *Interfaces*, 25:4, 104–113.

Courtois, P.-J. (1985) 'On Time and Space Decomposition of Complex Structures', *Communications of the ACM*, 28:6, 590–603.

Dietz, M. (1992) 'Outline of a Successful Simulation Project', *Industrial Engineering*, 24:11, 50–53.

Hoover, S.V. and Perry, R.F. (1990) *Simulation: A Problem-Solving Approach*. Reading, MA: Addison-Wesley.

Keller, L., Harrell, C. and Leavy, J. (1991) 'The Three Reasons Why Simulation Fails', *Industrial Engineering*, 23:4, 27–31.

Kleijnen, J.P.C. (1995) 'Verification and Validation of Simulation Models', *European Journal of Operational Research*, 82:1, 145–62.

Law, A.M. and Kelton, W.D. (2000) *Simulation Modeling and Analysis*, 3rd edn. New York: McGraw-Hill.

Law, A.M. and McComas, M.G. (1989) 'Pitfalls to Avoid in the Simulation of Manufacturing Systems', *Industrial Engineering*, 21:5, 28–69.

Law, A.M. and McComas, M.G. (1990) 'Secrets of Successful Simulation Studies', *Industrial Engineering*, 22:5, 47–72.

Paul, R.J. and Balmer, D. (1993) *Simulation Modelling*, Bromley, UK: Chartwell Bratt.

Pidd, M. (1991). 'Operations Research/Management Science Method', in *Operations Research in Management*, Littlechild, S.C. and Shutler M.F. (eds.). London: Prentice-Hall, 11–31.

Pidd, M. (1998) *Computer Simulation in Management Science*, 4th edn, Chichester, UK: Wiley.

Robinson, S. (1994a) *Successful Simulation: A Practical Approach to Simulation Projects*. Maidenhead, UK: McGraw-Hill.

Robinson, S. (1994b) 'Simulation Projects: Building the Right Conceptual Model', *Industrial Engineering*, 26:9, 34–6.

Robinson, S. (1995) An Heuristic Technique for Selecting the Run-Length of Non-Terminating Steady-State Simulations. *Simulation*, 65:3, pp. 170–9.

Robinson, S. (1999) 'Simulation Verification, Validation and Confidence', *Transactions of the Society for Computer Simulation International*, 16:2, 63–9.

Robinson, S., Lewis, C.D. and Brooks, R.J. (1999) 'An Heuristic Technique for Detecting the Output Characteristics of Discrete Event Simulation Models', in progress.

Robinson, S. and Pidd, M. (1998) 'Provider and Customer Expectations of Successful Simulation Projects', *Journal of the Operational Research Society*, 49:3, 200–9.

Sargent, R.G. (1982) 'Verification and Validation of Simulation Models', in Cellier, F.E. (ed.), *Progress in Modelling and Simulation*. London: Academic Press, 159–69.

Schultz, R.L. and Slevin, D.P. (1975) *Implementing Operations Research: Management Science*. New York: Elsevier.

Szymankiewicz, J., McDonald, J. and Turner, K. (1988) *Solving Business Problems by Simulation*. Maidenhead, UK: McGraw-Hill.

Ulgen, O. (1991) 'Proper Management Techniques are Keys to a Successful Simulation Project', *Industrial Engineering*, 23:8, 37–41.

Welch, P.D. (1983) 'The Statistical Analysis of Simulation Results', in Lavenberg, S. (ed.), *The Computer Performance Modeling Handbook*, New York: Academic Press. 268–328.

Willemain, T.R. (1994) 'Insights on Modeling from a Dozen Experts', *Operations Research*, 42: 2, 213–22.

Willemain, T.R. (1995) 'Model formulation: What Experts Think About and When', *Operations Research*, 43:6, 916–32.

5 Further Topics in Simulation

5.1 Introduction

Having given an overview of the main concepts in developing and using computer simulations, this chapter provides a quick tour of some more advanced simulation topics, and in particular those topics that are currently exercising the minds of researchers in the field. It is certainly not possible to give a detailed review of each subject, but simply an introduction and some pointers as to where to look for further information. The subject areas are split under two headings, those pertaining to modelling (conceptual modelling and model coding), and those pertaining to experimentation and analysis of the results.

5.2 Modelling

5.2.1 Conceptual modelling

The importance of the conceptual modelling stage in a simulation project has already been stressed in Section 4.3. The conceptual model is the specification of the model to be built and therefore affects the entire project. This task of deciding what aspects of the real system to include in the model and what to leave out is often regarded as more of an art than a science and one that modellers learn with experience. Although research in this area is in its infancy, the aim is to provide a better understanding of the advantages and disadvantages of the various different simulation models that could be built (Brooks and Tobias, 1996).

As Section 4.3 also indicated, there are many potential advantages of a simple model compared to a more complex one. Tilanus (1985) investigated the reasons given by operational researchers for the success and failure of projects using various OR techniques. He found that the use of a simple model was often mentioned as a reason for success. Ward (1989) also gives an interesting discussion of the benefits of simplicity in modelling. It can therefore be beneficial to attempt to simplify the model, either at the conceptual model stage or after it has been built. Some techniques for simplifying simulation models are given by Robinson (1994) in a business context, and by Innis and Rexstad (1983) in discussing more general applications. Further research in this area could lead to a clearer methodology for model simplification.

5.2.2 Object oriented simulation

Just as there has been a trend in computer science to move away from the traditional procedural approach to programming and adopt an object oriented approach, so computer simulation has followed suit. Indeed, it might be argued that discrete event simulation provided the original impetus for object orientation through SIMULA (Dahl and Nygaard, 1966), one of the first object oriented applications.

The structure of a typical simulation lends itself well to the concepts of object orientation, for instance, class mechanisms, encapsulation and polymorphism (Pidd, 1995). It is not the intention here to explain these concepts, which can be understood by reference to a book that specializes in the topic. A useful introduction to how the concepts of object orientation can be applied to simulations is provided by Joines and Roberts (1998). Meanwhile, many simulation software packages claim to have adopted an object oriented approach, although in practice few could be truly described as fully object oriented.

5.2.3 Simulation on more than one computer

Performing simulations on only one computer restricts the speed with which a simulation can be run to that provided by the fastest machine available. It also limits the number of users to those that can meaningfully sit round a computer screen in one geographical location. In order to break these time and space restrictions much interest is being placed in multi-computer and multi-user approaches to simulation modelling.

One such approach is known as *parallel and distributed simulation* (PADS) (Fujimoto, 1990; Nicol *et al.*, 1997). A number of connected computers are used in order to reduce the time taken to execute a simulation model run. In its simplest form this entails each computer performing a separate replication with the same model, the results being collected by a central computer. A more complex approach involves the events that make up a single simulation run being dispersed among the computers. Such an approach could prove very useful for large scale models where the execution time on a single computer is extremely slow. There are, however, a number of difficulties with developing an operational system of this nature, not least ensuring that the simulated events are synchronized.

Distributed interactive simulation (*DIS*) involves the real-time use of two or more simulation models that are geographically dispersed. The aim is to provide a training environment in which multiple users interact with a series of running simulation models. The best known example of this approach is the High Level Architecture (HLA) developed by the US Department of Defence, which aims to connect many thousands of simulations and their users, in real time to support training in military operations (Dahmann *et al.*, 1997). The HLA accomplishes this by dictating a communication standard that all simulations must adhere to and a technological infrastructure that connects the simulation in real time (the run time infrastructure). GRIDS (generic runtime infrastructure for distributed simulation) is another system that supports DIS, but is targeted for smaller simulations encountered in industry (Saville and Taylor, 1998).

The world-wide web obviously provides a mechanism for networking computers as an aid to simulation modelling, and so can help to support the type of approaches described above. As a result, interest has grown in *web-based simulation*. Among those that are investigating the possibilities of the web for simulation are Fishwick (1996), Page *et al.* (1997), Yücesan *et al.* (1998) and Pidd and Cassel (1998).

5.2.4 Virtual reality and simulation

Virtual reality (VR) is a possible extension to the animated graphics provided by visual interactive simulation systems (Grant and Lai, 1998). Indeed, a number of commercial software packages have started to include some 'virtual reality' capabilities, for instance, Quest (Barnes, 1996) and Witness (Markt and Mayer, 1997).

The benefits of virtual reality for simulation are unclear in that, in its present form, it does not provide a greater level of accuracy or an improved analysis of the output. What it does improve is the power of simulation as a communication tool, which is no doubt useful when presenting models to some audiences, but at the same time a significant amount of effort and computing power is required to develop and run a complex animation.

5.3 Experimentation and analysis

5.3.1 Variance reduction

In Section 4.5.1 it was shown that simulations need to be run for sufficiently long, and sufficient replications need to be performed, in order to obtain accurate results. For some models a great many replications are required, which in turn means that much time is needed for experimentation. The aim of variance reduction is to reduce this experimentation time by manipulating the random numbers sampled during a simulation run so that the results converge more quickly to their mean value.

A common approach is the use of antithetic random numbers, these being related to the original random numbers by:

Antithetic random number = 1 – original random number (5.1)

The idea is that if two simulation runs are performed, one with normal random sampling and the other with antithetic random sampling, then each should display approximately equal but opposite effects (for instance, a long breakdown in one run will be a short breakdown in the other). The average of the two runs should approximate to the average performance of the system. In practice, however, it cannot be guaranteed that this approach will work, not least because the complex interaction of many random events during a simulation run obscures any such effect.

Other methods of variance reduction exist, for instance, control variates, selective sampling and stratified sampling (Kleijnen, 1974). These ideas, however, seem to have limited application in practice.

5.3.2 Simulation optimization

In simulation experimentation much time can be spent searching for the values of the experimental factors that provide the optimum level of performance. For instance, the modeller may be searching for the maximum possible throughput from a manufacturing plant by changing the values of three or four different experimental variables. This can prove to be an extremely onerous task, particularly if the simulation requires long run times and there are many experimental factors. As a result, attention has turned to methods for speeding up and automating the process of optimizing the output of a simulation. For a useful review of simulation optimization see Carson and Maria (1997).

Figure 5.1 shows how the output from a simulation might vary as the value of a single experimental factor changes (this example is used because it can be represented on a two-dimensional graph). The resulting line is known as the 'response surface'. Assuming that the aim is to maximize the output from the simulation, then the optimum occurs at the highest peak. The difficulty facing the simulation modeller is to ensure that the highest peak is found with the minimum amount of effort. This is the aim of simulation optimization.

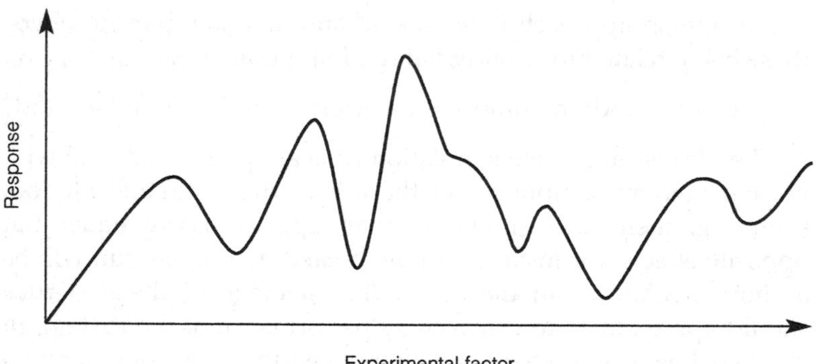

Figure 5.1 Simulation 'response surface' with one experimental factor

There are two main approaches to simulation optimization. In the first, the aim is to predict the shape of the response surface, use some means for describing it, and then apply an optimization method to find the highest peak (or lowest trough for minimization problems). By performing a series of carefully selected simulation runs, a basic profile of the response surface can be obtained. Various methods exist for describing the response surface. One method is to fit a regression equation to the data obtained from the model.

Another is to train a neural network (Hurrion, 1997). The regression equation has the advantage that the optimum can easily be found by use of differential calculus. The disadvantage is that if the response surface is particularly lumpy or discontinuous, it is not possible to find a simple equation that describes its shape. A neural network is able to manage almost any shape of response surface, but then there is no simple way of finding the optimum.

The second approach does not entail any prediction of the response surface, but uses heuristic search techniques (indeed, these could be applied to the neural network model of the response surface). At the simplest level if, say, an increase in an experimental factor leads to an improvement in the simulation's output, then the factor continues to be increased until no further improvement can be made. Although this approach guarantees that a peak (or trough) is reached, it does not guarantee that this is the highest peak (or lowest trough). As a result, more sophisticated techniques are used to try to find the 'global' optimum rather than just 'local' optima. Among these approaches are heuristic techniques such as simulated annealing, tabu search and genetic algorithms (Pidd, 1996).

It is this second approach that has been adopted by many simulation software suppliers who now provide simulation optimization packages. Because the optimization technique is embedded in the package, the simulation modellers do not have to concern themselves with the detailed workings of the method. Instead, they simply need to specify the key parameters on which the model should be optimized. This normally entails providing an objective function (for example, maximize throughput, minimize cost) and a list of experimental factors and their limits. The software will then automatically search for an optimum. A cautionary word: these optimizers cannot guarantee that the global optimum will be found. What they will provide is a search of the response surface and an indication of where a good result will lie. Indeed, a better title for these optimizers might be 'searchizers'. Their success in finding a good solution is largely dependent on how much time they have to perform their search. The stochastic nature of most simulation models further complicates the search process.

5.3.3 Output analysis

Some of the concepts of output analysis are discussed in Section 4.5, the aim being to ensure that the estimates of a system's performance obtained from a simulation are as accurate as possible. As such, it is important to determine a suitable warm-up period for a model and a suitable run-length and number of replications. A number of methods for identifying a warm-up period have been proposed, for instance, Goldsman *et al.* (1994), Kelton (1989), Schruben (1982) and Schruben *et al.* (1983), as well as the popular method of Welch (1983) mentioned in Section 4.5.1.

Section 4.5.1 stressed the use of multiple replications for obtaining a confidence interval as an estimate of a system's performance. This is known as the replication-deletion method, because it consists of a series of *replications* from which the warm-up period is *deleted*. Alternative approaches exist for determining a confidence interval, most of which involve performing a single long run, for instance, the regenerative method (Crane and Iglehart, 1974a, 1974b, 1975; Fishman, 1973, 1974), the batch means method (Law and Carson, 1979) and the standardized time-series method (Schruben, 1983). An introduction to all these methods is provided in Law and Kelton (2000).

References and further reading

Barnes, M. (1996) 'Virtual Reality and Simulation', Charnes, J.M., Morrice, D.J., Brunner, D.T. and Swain, J.J., (eds), *Proceedings of the 1996 Winter Simulation Conference*, Institute of Electrical and Electronics Engineers, Piscataway, NJ, 101–110.

Brooks, R.J. and Tobias, A.M. (1996) 'Choosing the Best Model: Level of Detail, Complexity and Model Performance', *Mathematical and Computer Modelling*, 24:4, 1–14.

Carson, Y. and Maria, A. (1997) 'Simulation Optimization: Methods and Applications', Andradóttir, S., Healy, K.J., Withers, D.H. and Nelson, B.L., (eds), *Proceedings of the 1997 Winter Simulation Conference*, Institute of Electrical and Electronics Engineers, Piscataway, NJ, 118–26.

Crane, M.A. and Iglehart, D.L. (1974a), 'Simulating Stable Stochastic Systems, I: General Multiserver Queues', *Journal of the ACM*, 21, 103–13.

Crane, M.A. and Iglehart, D.L. (1974b), 'Simulating Stable Stochastic Systems, II: Markov Chains', *Journal of the ACM*, 21, 114–23.

Crane, M.A. and Iglehart, D.L. (1975), 'Simulating Stable Stochastic Systems, III: Regenerative Processes and Discrete-Event Simulations', *Operations Research*, 23, 33–45.

Dahl, O. and Nygaard, K. (1966) 'SIMULA: An Algol-Based Simulation Language', *Communications of the ACM*, 9, 671–78.

Dahmann, J.S., Fujimoto, R.M. and Weatherly, R.M. (1997) 'The Department of Defense High Level Architecture', Andradóttir, S., Healy, K.J., Withers, D.H. and

Nelson, B.L., (eds), *Proceedings of the 1997 Winter Simulation Conference*, Institute of Electrical and Electronics Engineers, Piscataway, NJ, 142–9.

Fishman, G.S. (1973) 'Statistical Analysis for Queueing Simulations', *Management Science*, 20, 363–9.

Fishman, G.S. (1974) 'Estimation of Multiserver Queueing Simulations', *Operations Research*, 22, 72–8.

Fishwisk, P.A. (1996). Web-Based Simulation: Some Personal Observations', Charnes, J.M., Morrice, D.J., Brunner, D.T. and Swain, J.J. (eds), *Proceedings of the 1996 Winter Simulation Conference*, Institute of Electrical and Electronics Engineers, Piscataway, NJ, 772–9.

Fujimoto, R.M. (1990) 'Parallel Discrete Event Simulation', *Communications of the ACM*, 33:10, 30–53.

Goldsman, D., Schruben, L.W. and Swain, J.J. (1994). 'Tests for the Transient Mean in Simulated Time Series', *Naval Research Logistics*, 41, 171–87.

Grant, H. and Lai, C.K. (1998) 'Simulation Modeling with Artificial Reality Technology (SMART): An Integration of Virtual Reality and Simulation Modeling', Medeiros, D.J., Watson, E.F., Manivannan, M. and Carson, J. (eds), Proceedings of the 1998 Winter Simulation Conference, *Institute of Electrical and Electronics Engineers*, Piscataway, NJ, 437–41.

Hurrion, R.D. (1997) 'An Example of Simulation Optimization Using a Neural Network Metamodel: Finding the Optimum Number of Kanbans in a Manufacturing System', *Journal of the Operational Research Society*, 48:11, 1105–12.

Innis, G.S., and Rexstad, E. (1983) 'Simulation Model Simplification Techniques', *Simulation*, 41:1, 7–15.

Joines, J.A. and Roberts, S.D. (1998) 'Fundamentals of Object-Oriented Simulation', Medeiros, D.J., Watson, E.F., Manivannan, M. and Carson, J. (eds), *Proceedings of the 1998 Winter Simulation Conference*, Institute of Electrical and Electronics Engineers, Piscataway, NJ, 141–9.

Kelton, W.D. (1989) 'Random Initialization Methods in Simulation', *IIE Transactions*, 21, 355–67.

Kleijnen, J.P.C. (1974) *Statistical Techniques in Simulation*, vols 1 and 2, New York: Marcel Dekker.

Law, A.M. and Carson, J.S. (1979) 'A Sequential Procedure for Determining the Length of a Steady-State Simulation', *Operations Research*, 27, 1011–25.

Law, A.M. and Kelton, W.D. (2000) *Simulation Modeling and Analysis*, 3rd edn. New York: McGraw-Hill.

Markt, P.M. and Mayer, M.H. (1997) 'Witness Simulation Software: A Flexible Suit of Simulation Tools', Andradóttir, S., Healy, K.J., Withers, D.H. and Nelson, B.L., (eds), *Proceedings of the 1997 Winter Simulation Conference*, Institute of Electrical and Electronics Engineers, Piscataway, NJ, 711–17.

Nicol, D.M., Johnson, M.M. and Yoshimura, A.S. (1997) 'The IDES Framework: A Case Study in Development of a Parallel Discrete-Event Simulation System', Andradóttir, S., Healy, K.J., Withers, D.H. and Nelson, B.L., (eds), *Proceedings of the 1997 Winter Simulation Conference*, Institute of Electrical and Electronics Engineers, Piscataway, NJ, 93–9.

Page, E.H., Moose, R.L. and Griffin, S.P. (1997) 'Web-Based Simulation in SimJava using Remote Method Invocation', Andradóttir, S., Healy, K.J., Withers, D.H. and Nelson, B.L., (eds), *Proceedings of the 1997 Winter Simulation Conference*, Institute of Electrical and Electronics Engineers, Piscataway, NJ, 468–74.

Pidd, M. (1995) 'Object-Orientation, Discrete Simulation and the Three-Phase Approach', *Journal of the Operational Research Society*, 46:3, 362–74.

Pidd, M. (1996) *Tools for Thinking: Modelling in Management Science*. Chichester, UK: Wiley.

Pidd, M. and Cassel, R.A. (1998) 'Three Phase Simulation in Java', Medeiros, D.J., Watson, E.F., Manivannan, M. and Carson, J. (eds), *Proceedings of the 1998 Winter Simulation Conference*, Institute of Electrical and Electronics Engineers, Piscataway, NJ, 367–71.

Robinson, S. (1994) *Successful Simulation: A Practical Approach to Simulation Projects*. Maidenhead, UK: McGraw-Hill.

Saville J. and Taylor S.J.E. (1998) 'Developing Interest Management Techniques in Distributed Interactive Simulation Using Java', Zobel R. and Moeller D, (eds), *Proceedings of the 12th European Simulation Multiconference 1998*, The Society for Computer Simulation International, Delft, 272–8.

Schruben, L.W. (1982) 'Detecting Initialization Bias in Simulation Output', *Operations Research*, 30,569-590.

Schruben, L.W. (1983) 'Confidence Interval Estimation Using Standardized Time Series', *Operations Research*, 31, 1090–1108.

Schruben, L.W., Singh, H. and Tierney, L. (1983) 'Optimal Tests for Initialization Bias in Simulation Output', *Operations Research*, 31, 1167–78.

Tilanus, C.B. (1985) 'Failures and Successes of Quantitative Methods in Management', *European Journal of Operational Research*, 19, 170–5.

Ward, S.C. (1989) 'Arguments for constructively simple models', *Journal of Operational Research Society*, 40:2, 141–53.

Welch, P.D. (1983) 'The Statistical Analysis of Simulation Results', in Lavenberg, S. (ed.), *The Computer Performance Modeling Handbook*. New York: Academic Press, 268–328.

Yücesan, E., Chen, C.H. and Lee, I. (1998) 'Web-Based Simulation Experiments', Medeiros, D.J., Watson, E.F., Manivannan, M. and Carson, J.(eds), *Proceedings of the 1998 Winter Simulation Conference*, Institute of Electrical and Electronics Engineers, Piscataway, NJ, 1649–54.

6 Conclusion

Simulation is a powerful and flexible modelling approach and in surveys it is often found to be the most commonly used Operational Research technique (Law and Kelton, 2000). It is used in many industries – for example, the Winter Simulation Conference (www.wintersim.org), which is one of the main simulation conferences, usually includes presentations on applications of simulation in manufacturing, service industries, the military, health care, transportation and telecommunications. Simulation is also used in scientific disciplines such as physics, biology and environmental sciences.

Important features that can be included in a simulation model include:

- Many different entities
- Complex behaviour of the entities
- Complex interactions between the entities
- Randomness to simulate variability
- Standard and empirical probability distributions
- Conditions that change over time
- A visual display of the behaviour of the model
- An ability to experiment with the model by changing any part of it
- An ability to collect a variety of statistics to measure the performance of the simulated system.

However, it should not be assumed automatically that simulation is the best approach to a particular problem. Part of the conceptual modelling stage of an Operational Research project should be to consider not only what to include in the model, but also what type of model is best suited to the problem. For example, many problems for which simulation is considered concern the analysis of a queueing system. An alternative approach is therefore to use queueing theory, which has the advantage that it may be able to give an analytical solution. However, the assumptions required for queueing theory are too limiting for many real world situations.

If simulation is chosen as the modelling tool for the problem, modern VIMS simulation software packages (Chapter 3) can sometimes make building a simulation model reasonably straightforward, at least if the model fits within the designed application of the package. Much of the skill in carrying out a successful simulation project then becomes translating the real-world problem into an appropriate model and effectively testing the model, experimenting with it and analysing the results (Chapter 4). An essential basis for this is to have a good understanding of how the model works (Chapter 2).

One distinctive characteristic of simulation is that it is an experimental approach rather than one that gives an optimal solution. As part of this process, one aim of simulation should always be to improve the understanding of the system. A key aspect of this is the ability to examine what is happening in detail within different parts of the simulation model. It is very satisfying to gain a new insight into a system in this way that then illuminates the problem being tackled.

Our aim in this book has been to provide a good foundation for the effective use of simulation as a tool for decision-making. Solving a problem using simulation can be a fruitful and enjoyable experience. The successful application of simulation requires a range of skills from a creative approach in model formulation and choice of experiments to a logical approach in constructing the model and analysing the results. We hope that you get the opportunity to develop these skills further by building and applying simulation models in practice.

References and further reading

Law, A.M. and Kelton, W.D. (2000) *Simulation Modeling and Analysis*, 3rd edn. New York: McGraw-Hill.

Appendices

Appendix I

Algorithms for random number generators

The most commonly used approach for random number generators is to use the linear or multiplicative congruential method. The linear version uses three integer constants a, m and c. It produces a sequence of integers that are used to generate the random numbers. The algorithm obtains the next integer in the sequence by taking the current integer and multiplying it by a, and then by adding c. It then finds the remainder when this value is divided by m, and this remainder becomes the next integer. Algebraically, denoting the jth integer by I_j,

$$I_j = (aI_{j-1} + c) \bmod m \qquad \text{(A1)}$$

The integers I_j are all between 0 and m–1. When the function is called, the algorithm calculates the next integer and then converts it to a number between 0 and 1 by dividing it by m. This number is returned as the new random number. The only difference with the multiplicative version is that $c = 0$.

These generators can only produce the numbers 0, $1/m$, $2/m$, and so on up to $(m-1)/m$. However, provided m is large, the gaps between these numbers will be very small and so this will not usually be an important drawback. In order for this type of generator to work well it is vital that good values are chosen for the constants. For example, constants found to work reasonably well for the multiplicative version are $a = 16\,807$ and $m = 2^{31} - 1 = 2\,147\,483\,647$ (Press *et al.*, 1992).

Reference

Press, W.H., Teukolsky, S.A., Vetterling, W.T. and Flannery, B.P. (1992) *Numerical Recipes in C: The Art of Scientific Computing*, 2nd edn. Cambridge University Press.

Appendix II

Formula for sampling from the negative exponential distribution

For the negative exponential, the cumulative probability, $F(x)$, is given by:

$$F(x) = 1 - e^{\frac{-x}{\mu}} \qquad \text{(A2)}$$

where μ is the mean of the distribution. So, given a random number, r, the value to be chosen from the distribution is the value x such that $F(x) = r$. So,

$$1 - e^{\frac{-x}{\mu}} = r$$

$$e^{\frac{-x}{\mu}} = 1 - r$$

$$\frac{-x}{\mu} = \ln(1 - r)$$

$$x = -\mu \ln(1 - r) \qquad \text{(A3)}$$

where ln is the natural logarithm.

Note that $1 - r$ is a random number between 0 and 1 just like r and so an alternative, slightly simpler, formula that could be used instead is $x = -\mu\ln(r)$. Formula A3 is preferred because small values of r then correspond to small values of x.

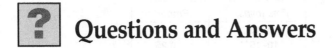

Questions and Answers

Chapter 2

2.1 Choose an everyday task such as cooking a meal, making a cup of tea or driving the car on a short journey and describe it using states and events. Explain how you could simplify the description or make it more detailed.

2.2 The casualty department of a hospital uses a triage system whereby patients have a short initial examination carried out by a nurse. The nurse classifies the injuries as serious, minor or requiring no treatment, with patients in the latter category being sent home. About 5 per cent of patients have serious injuries and about 50 per cent have minor injuries. Serious patients are seen as soon as possible by an experienced junior doctor. Minor patients can be seen by either an experienced junior doctor or an inexperienced junior doctor. What are the entities in this system? Identify the states and events and write the event details for each event.

2.3 Choose any retail establishment such as a supermarket, restaurant or pub. Identify the entities and draw an activity cycle diagram for a model to simulate the queueing and serving behaviour.

2.4 Why do conditional events usually cause a bound event to be added to the event list?

2.5 Find the next five sample values for the following probability distributions. Work to one decimal place and use the 10th row of the random number table (Table 2.6):

(a) Negative exponential distribution with a mean of 10.
(b) Uniform distribution between 3 and 11.
(c) The following empirical distribution (assuming that values are uniformly distributed within each interval).

Time (mins)	*Proportion*
5–10	0.10
10–15	0.25
15–20	0.30
20–25	0.20
25–30	0.15

2.6 Using the top hat method allocate random numbers to the following empirical distribution of 500 purchases in a clothing store (the number of items will be used to determine time spent in the store and time spent at the checkout)

No. of items bought	*No. of people*
1	97
2	221
3	143
4	39

Using the 5th row of the random number table choose four values from this distribution.

2.7 What is the advantage of using different random number streams for different sources of variability?

2.8 What is the purpose of the event list in the three-phase approach? Why does the event list just contain the next events for each entity and not any events further into the future?

2.9 Re-run the bank simulation for the first 15 minutes using random numbers starting from the 15th row of the random number table. Explain why the results are different to those in Table 2.22 and what implications this has for model experimentation.

Chapter 3

3.1 The terms Visual Interactive Simulation (VIS) and Visual Interactive Modelling (VIM) are often used to describe modern simulation software packages. Explain these terms and discuss the benefits of using VIS and VIM for simulation modelling.

Chapter 4

4.1 An organization has just purchased a simulation package and some members of staff have been selected to use the software. Assuming that these members of staff have no previous simulation experience describe the training you believe they would require to use the software effectively.

4.2 The availability of accurate data is a necessity for any simulation study, and yet they can prove extremely difficult to obtain. How can accurate data be obtained and what can be done to overcome shortcomings in the data that are available?

4.3 The validity of a simulation model is vital to the success of a simulation study. Discuss the meaning of validity and how it might be achieved during the delivery of a simulation project.

4.4 When simulation experiments are being performed careful thought should be given to the warm-up period, run-length and number of replications performed. How can each of these be determined?

4.5 The following table shows the results (mean waiting time for customers at a bank) obtained from 20 replications with a simulation model. By calculating confidence intervals, provide advice on the number of replications that are required to obtain a satisfactory result.

Replication	Mean waiting time (mins)	Replication	Mean waiting time (mins)
1	24.20	11	27.75
2	21.71	12	23.41
3	18.41	13	26.20
4	21.33	14	24.01
5	26.22	15	23.05
6	27.68	16	25.67
7	25.83	17	23.53
8	25.48	18	18.68
9	22.99	19	26.43
10	24.30	20	19.10

4.6 For Further Research: investigate and describe the various methods for performing the following:

- Fitting statistical distributions to empirical data.
- Determining the warm-up period of a steady-state simulation model.
- Variance reduction.
- Analysing the output of steady-state simulations.

4.7 Build a simulation model of the bank described in Section 2.7. By experimenting with the model and analysing the results make recommendations as to the best operating policy for the bank. State any assumptions that you make.

4.8 Case Question: MacDuff's Fast Food Restaurant

As part of their expansion programme MacDuff's Fast Food Ltd are planning to open a new restaurant. The layout is shown below. They have some concerns over their plans for the restaurant and so they have asked for a computer simulation to be developed.

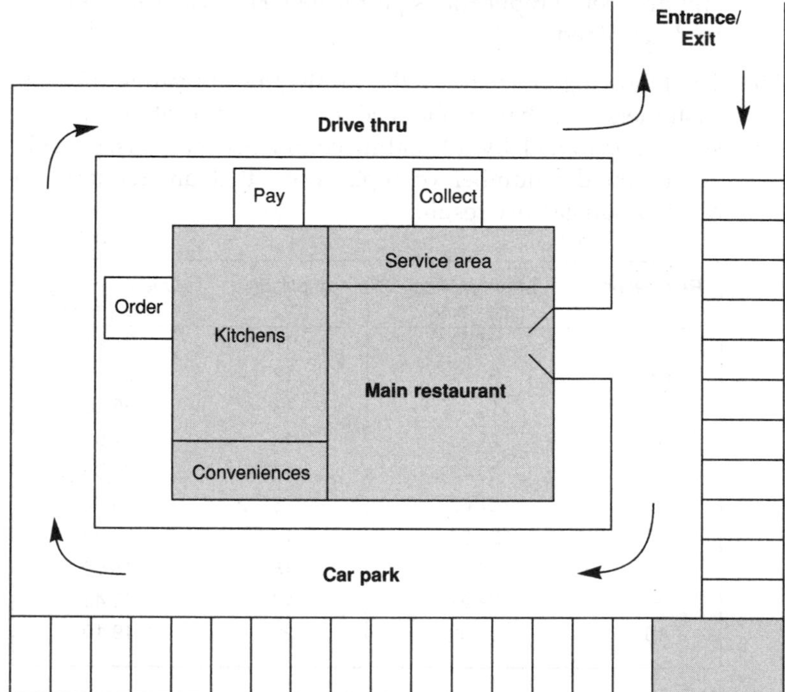

This simulation should address one or more of the following issues:

- The number of service points required.
- The number of staff required and the design of staff jobs and rosters.
- The number of tables required.
- The space required for queuing between 'drive thru' service points.
- The effects of changes in demand.

MacDuff's have provided the following information to help in the development of the model.

(a) Opening hours: 08:00 – 23:00, 7 days/week.

(b) Customer arrival rates (the same each day of the week):

In restaurant Drive thru			
Hour	*Average customer groups per hour*	*Hour*	*Average cars per hour*
08:00 – 09:00	80	08:00 – 12:00	86
09:00 – 10:00	120	12:00 – 16:00	100
10:00 – 11:00	80	16:00 – 20:00	120
11:00 – 12:00	60	20:00 – 23:00	75
12:00 – 13:00	150		
13:00 – 14:00	200		
14:00 – 15:00	80		
15:00 – 16:00	75		
16:00 – 17:00	75		
17:00 – 18:00	200		
18:00 – 19:00	300		
19:00 – 20:00	200		
20:00 – 21:00	150		
21:00 – 22:00	80		
22:00 – 23:00	60		

(c) Number of customers in customer groups:

Number of customers in a group	*Probability*
1	10
2	20
3	20
4	30
5	15
6	5

(d) Restaurant:

Number of service points: 3
Mean service time per customer: 0.5 mins (Erlang distribution, K=3).
Number of tables: 18 (tables are of sufficient capacity to seat any group size; only one customer group will sit at any one table).
Average time at a table: 10 mins (Erlang distribution, K=3).

(e) Drive thru:

Service point 1 (order): average service time: 0.5 mins (Erlang distribution, K=3).
Service point 2 (pay): average service time: 0.25 mins (negative exponential).
Service point 3 (collect): average service time: 0.3 mins (normal, st. dev. = 0.03).

(f) Service staff: 5 all day (operate the restaurant service counter and drive thru).

(g) Financial data:

Staff cost: £11.47 per hour.
Average revenue/customer: £7.62.
Material costs: 30 per cent of revenue/customer.
Overheads: 30 per cent of revenue/customer.

Select a set of issues to address and using a suitable simulation package develop and test a simulation model of the MacDuff's restaurant. Perform a series of experiments with the model and provide a summary report of your key findings and recommendations.

Chapter 5

5.1 Parallel and distributed simulation (PADS) and distributed interactive simulation (DIS) have largely been developed for large scale military applications. Consider how they might be useful to simulation users in the business community.

Answers

2.1 The description can be made more detailed by adding events to split states and can be made less detailed by combining states to eliminate events. For example, making a cup of tea could include the states *take kettle to tap* and *fill kettle with water* with the event *arrive at tap* between. This could be simplified by combining the two states into a single state *take kettle to tap and fill with water*. The description could be made more detailed by dividing the state *fill kettle with water* into the states *move kettle under tap, turn tap on, water pouring into kettle, turn tap off, move kettle away from tap* dividing these states with the events *start turn tap on, finish turn tap on, start turn tap off,* and *finish turn tap off*.

2.2 The entities are the patients, nurses, experienced doctors and inexperienced doctors. States of the patients are *elsewhere, queue for nurse, examined by nurse, serious queue, minor queue, treated by exp. doctor, treated by inexp. doctor*. States for the doctors and nurses are *busy* and *idle*. The event details are:

Event	***Type***	***Conditions for event to occur***	***Change in state caused by event***	***Future events to schedule***
Arrival	Bound		Add new patient to queue for nurse.	Next *arrival*
Start triage	Conditional	Nurse is *idle* and there is a patient in queue for nurse.	Nurse becomes *busy* and customer is in state *examined by nurse.*	*Finish triage*
Finish triage	Bound		Nurse becomes *idle.* A random number is chosen to decide on the state of the patient which is either *serious queue, minor queue* or *elsewhere.*	
Start exp	Conditional	Experienced doctor is *idle* and there is a patient waiting in either the *serious queue* or the *minor queue.*	Doctor becomes *busy.* A patient is chosen in order of preference from *serious queue, minor queue* and becomes *treated by exp. doctor.*	*Finish exp*
Finish exp	Bound		Doctor becomes *idle* and patient leaves to state *elsewhere.*	

▶

Event	Type	Conditions for event to occur	Change in state caused by event	Future events to schedule
Start inexp	Conditional	Inexperienced doctor is *idle* and there is a patient in the *minor queue.*	Doctor becomes *busy* and patient becomes *treated by inexp. doctor.*	*Finish inexp*
Finish inexp	Bound		Doctor becomes *idle* and patient leaves to state *elsewhere.*	

2.4 Conditional events usually occur at the start of an active state (or activity). Part of such a conditional event is generally to choose the duration of the activity and to schedule the end of the activity after this duration as a bound event on the event list.

2.5 (a) Using equation 2.1, $x = -10\ln(1-r)$. Five random numbers between 0 and 1 can be obtained by taking four digits for each number from the tenth row of the random number table to give 0.5806, 0.8295, 0.2600, 0.9128, 0.9934. Putting these into the equation generates the five sample values 8.7, 17.7, 3.0, 24.4, 50.2.

(b) Using equation 2.2, $x = 3+8r$. The same five random numbers as in (a) then give the sample values 7.6, 9.6, 5.1, 10.3, 10.9. (Alternatively, three digits could be used for the random numbers as this is enough precision in this case).

(c) The random numbers allocated to the five categories are 01–10, 11–35, 36–65, 66–85, 86–00. Once a category is chosen, a value from the uniform distribution between 0 and 5 is required to choose a value within the category (using the equation $x = 5r$). As before, four digits have been used for the random number between 0 and 1. For the first value, 58 gives category 15–20 and then 0682 gives 0.3 for the uniform distribution value, so the final value is 15.3. For the next value, 95 gives category 25–30 and 2600 gives 1.3 so the value is 26.3. Following this procedure the next three values obtained are 26.4, 13.8 and 7.8.

2.6 Three random digits are required to produce a number between 1 and 1000 (taking 000 to be 1000). We could use the numbers 1–500 and allocate them according to the frequencies using 001–097, 098–318, 319–461, 462–500.

This means numbers above 500 have to be ignored. The first

number in row 5 is 652 so this is ignored and the next number 430 used to give a value of 3 items. The next 3 values chosen in this way use random numbers 117, 460, 269 to give values 2, 3, 2.

However, a more efficient approach is to allocate the numbers according to twice the frequencies so that all the numbers 1–1000 are used and none have to be ignored. The allocation is then 001–194, 195–636, 637–922, 923–000. The first four random numbers are 652, 430, 117, 654 which give values 3, 2, 1, 3.

2.7 Alternative scenarios can then be run using the same random numbers as far as possible. Corresponding runs can be directly compared, with differences in the results being mainly due to the different conditions rather than random variation. This can show the effect of the change in conditions much more clearly.

2.8 The event list gives the times at which the future scheduled events will occur. This enables the simulation executive to determine which event will happen next. The amount of information that has to be kept is reduced by only looking one step ahead. It is also usually not possible to determine the events any further ahead without running the simulation. The event list keeps being updated one step at a time which allows the simulation to carry on running until the user decides to stop it.

2.9

State					**Statistics**
Time	*Queue*	*Senior*	*Junior*	*Additional*	*Queue time*
0.0	empty	idle	idle	off-duty	
1.8	C1	idle	idle	off-duty	
1.8	empty	C1	idle	off-duty	0.0
2.2	C2	C1	idle	off-duty	
2.2	empty	C1	C2	off-duty	0.0
5.5	empty	C1	idle	off-duty	
5.8	empty	idle	idle	off-duty	
7.5	C3	idle	idle	off-duty	
7.5	empty	C3	idle	off-duty	0.0
7.7	C4	C3	idle	off-duty	
7.7	empty	C3	C4	off-duty	0.0
8.5	C5	C3	C4	off-duty	
10.0	C6,C5	C3	C4	off-duty	
10.7	C7,C6,C5	C3	C4	off-duty	
10.7	C7,C6	C3	C4	C5	2.2
11.3	C7,C6	idle	C4	C5	
11.3	C7	C6	C4	C5	1.3
11.5	C8,C7	C6	C4	C5	
13.0	C8,C7	C6	C4	idle	

Event list			**Random numbers**
Event	*Time*	*Done*	
Arrival C1	1.8	✓	70 85
Arrival C2	2.2	✓	24 45
Finish serve S	5.8	✓	64 03
Arrival C3	7.5	✓	96 99
Finish serve J	5.5	✓	32 33
Arrival C4	7.7	✓	14 81
Finish serve S	11.3	✓	41 83
Arrival C5	8.5	✓	41 05
Finish serve J	15.8		94 10
Arrival C6	10.0	✓	63 13
Arrival C7	10.7	✓	36 30
Arrival C8	11.5	✓	41 26
Finish serve A	13.0	✓	27 32
Finish serve S	17.8		90 51
Arrival C9	13.5	✓	74 28
Finish serve A	18.7		70 73
Arrival C10	15.2		67 08

▶

State					Statistics
Time	*Queue*	*Senior*	*Junior*	*Additional*	*Queue time*
13.0	C8	C6	C4	C7	2.3
13.5	C9,C8	C6	C4	C7	

Note that at time 13.0 the additional teller finishes serving customer five. In the hand simulation in Chapter 2, the additional teller went off-duty after serving a customer as there was no queue. Here, since there are two customers waiting when *finish serve A* is performed, the additional teller becomes *idle* rather than *off-duty*. Therefore, in the C phase *start serve A* can take place for C7.

The results are different to those in Table 2.22 because different random numbers are used. In the same way, the behaviour will be different each day in the real system. It is very important to run the model several times with different random numbers in order to take account of the variability in the system (see Section 4.5). The results from just one run may not be typical of the system behaviour.

4.5 The table opposite shows the 95 per cent confidence intervals for 2 to 20 replications. The 'percentage deviation' is the width of the interval around the mean. The graph shows how the confidence interval narrows as the number of replications increases (the solid line showing the cumulative mean average and the dashed lines showing the upper and lower confidence intervals).

The number of replications required depends on what is meant by a 'satisfactory' result. If an interval that is within ±10 per cent of the mean is sufficiently accurate, then eight or nine replications would be required. However, for a more accurate result of, say, within ±5 per cent of the mean, more than 20 replications would be required.

Replication	Results	Cum. mean average	Standard deviation	Confidence interval Lower interval	Upper interval	Percentage deviation
1	24.20	24.20	n/a	n/a	n/a	n/a
2	21.71	22.95	1.761	7.13	38.77	68.93
3	18.41	21.44	2.901	14.23	28.65	33.61
4	21.33	21.41	2.369	17.64	25.18	17.60
5	26.22	22.37	2.972	18.68	26.06	16.49
6	27.68	23.26	3.430	19.66	26.86	15.48
7	25.83	23.63	3.278	20.59	26.66	12.83
8	25.48	23.86	3.105	21.26	26.45	10.88
9	22.99	23.76	2.919	21.52	26.01	9.44
10	24.30	23.82	2.757	21.84	25.79	8.28
11	27.75	24.17	2.873	22.24	26.10	7.98
12	23.41	24.11	2.748	22.36	25.86	7.24
13	26.20	24.27	2.694	22.64	25.90	6.71
14	24.91	24.32	2.594	22.82	25.81	6.16
15	23.05	24.23	2.521	22.84	25.63	5.76
16	25.67	24.32	2.462	23.01	25.63	5.39
17	23.53	24.27	2.391	23.04	25.50	5.07
18	18.68	23.96	2.668	22.64	25.29	5.54
19	26.43	24.09	2.654	22.81	25.37	5.31
20	19.10	23.84	2.815	22.50	25.16	5.52

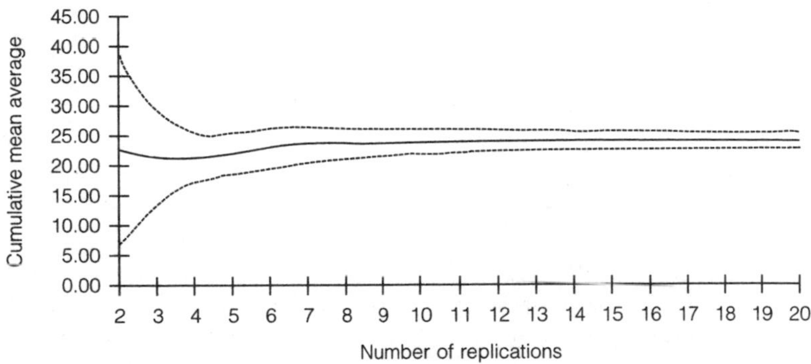

Inventory Control

Colin Lewis

Foreword

THIS half-book describes that material in the subject area of inventory control and its associated subject of demand forecasting which underpin the majority of practical applications in industry, business and service organizations.

Thus the demand forecasting material covered in Chapters 8 and 9, as a prerequisite to inventory control, concentrates on the development of the family of forecasting models based on the simple exponentially weighted average with its advantages of:

- Computational cheapness.
- Robustness and ability to be monitored so that 'out of control' situations can be readily detected.
- Ease of 'starting up' when initializing new items with no previous demand history.
- Adaptability in terms of changing sensitivity in line with the characteristic of the demand data encountered, and
- Flexibility in terms of ability to cope with stationary, growth and seasonality.

Chapters 10 to 12 cover material relating to the most commonly used inventory policy, the re-order level policy in which stocks are reviewed continuously and a relatively fixed replenishment order placed when stock-on-hand falls to or below a specified level.

Chapter 13 covers material relating to the next most popular inventory policy, the re-order cycle policy in which stocks are reviewed at fixed intervals of time at which time a replenishment order is placed whose size is calculated as that which would bring stocks back up to a nominal maximum level , if there were no delay in that order's delivery.

Finally, Chapter 14 discusses Pareto or ABC analysis as a suitable vehicle for allocating inventory policies to the most appropriate stocked item or service.

Colin Lewis
Solihull
March 2000

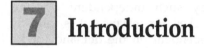

7 Introduction

Most businesses or organizations which produce goods or offer services need to hold inventories to maintain a reasonable level of service to their customers and clients while, at the same time, controlling the levels of those inventories such that their operating costs (all those costs associated with holding inventories – see page 134 for details) do not become prohibitive. Hence, in broad terms, inventory control can be regarded as the science-based art of controlling the amount of inventory (or stock) held, in various forms, within a business or organization to meet the demands placed upon that business or organization at a cost which does not become excessive. Too much inventory clearly offers customers an excellent level of service, but will eventually bankrupt the stockholder. Alternatively, too little inventory minimizes costs for the stockholder but offers customers such a poor level of service that eventually they are likely to take their business elsewhere. Thus inventory control is a perpetual balancing exercise attempting to:

- Meet the demand of customers by offering them a reasonable level of service, such that most of the time their demands on the inventory system can be met immediately, while
- Not involving the stockholder in excessive costs.

One of the first steps in establishing the amount of inventory of goods or services that should be held is to estimate the future demand to which those inventories are likely to be subjected. Clearly, the higher the demand the more inventory that will be required to fulfill that demand at a reasonable level of service to customers.

Types of demand imposed on inventory systems

Inventory control systems are designed primarily to cope with independent demand situations. Independent demand describes the type of demand for a product or service which is *independent* of the demand for other apparently related products or services. Virtually all service organizations, public utilities and retail and wholesale organizations display such independent demand characteristics. Within a supermarket, for instance, it is unlikely that the demand for bread is dependent on the demand for ice cream. Also, even within manufacturing environments – where demand at lower levels of the production process are clearly dependent on demand at higher levels – from a inventory point of view it may be more sensible to ignore this self-evident dependency and assume that trends identified in past demand data – using a forecasting procedure – could be a more reliable (and certainly a more cost effective) indicator of future demand (that is, it is assumed that demand is *independent*).

However, generally it has to be admitted that within manufacturing organizations primarily concerned with assembly – where a planned level of production of finished products is the norm – the demand for sub-assemblies, components and raw materials that make up the finished product is clearly highly *dependent* on that planned level of production. Hence in automobile manufacture, the forecast of demand for wheels, tyres and so on, is essentially more likely to be a multiple of five times the demand for completed vehicles (that is, four road wheels plus a spare) rather than a projection of previous demand at the component level. The method of controlling the provisioning of sub-assemblies, components and raw materials for such dependent demand situations, now generally referred to as 'supply chain management' which includes such techniques as Material Requirements Planning (MRP) and Just-in-Time (JIT), is radically different from that for independent demand and is not covered in this half-book.

However, even within a dependent demand environment, at the lower levels of demand in a production process, rather than relying on an expensive and complicated database MRP exercise – which involves the process of exploding and aggregating demand over several levels of production – if past demand can be assumed to be a reasonable indicator of future demand (that is, demand can be assumed to be independent) stocks held by traditional inventory control policies with parameters established through a forecasting regime may well be more cost effective than MRP, JIT and so on. Certainly no automotive manufacturer establishes the demand for the many standard nuts, bolts, washers and fasteners through an aggregation process – even though technically it should be possible. Even for such relatively cheap items, however, it is still necessary that the inventory policies which are used to control such items do so effectively with a very high level of service (so that production is never halted due to the lack of a relatively cheap item) but at a reasonable cost.

However, in general the material in this half-book applies to the holding of inventory of items or services where the demand is at the item or service level. While this may exclude that sector of the manufacturing industry based on the production of complex units or assemblies (such as automotive production), where the demand at the component level is directly related to production of units or assemblies at the top level, it does not exclude that sector of manufacturing where the end product is relatively simple in terms of constituent components.

Examples of inventory control situations where the ordering of replenishments to re-stock inventories is controlled by parameters determined by forecasts of demand and costs of inventory operations are:

- Supermarkets and, with the ever decreasing costs of *data capture*, increasingly a majority of retail outlets. The sometimes annoying insistence of the operating systems operating in these environments, which ensure that every transaction is recorded through the *data capture* system (cash till), is as much to ensure accurate stock recording as to prevent theft or fraud.
- Bars and pubs where pumps are metered and again all transactions must pass through the cash till to ensure accurate stock recording.
- Utilities such as gas and water, but excluding electricity which cannot be stored other than on a miniscule basis in pumped storage systems. Here measurements of usage have yet to become automatic, such that estimates (forecasts) have to be used if meter readers cannot gain access.
- Stockists and wholesalers in virtually all sections of manufacture and distribution who act as intermediate stockholders between manufacturers and those customers whose demand requirements are not large enough to justify direct dealing with the manufacturer. Steel stockholders and builders' merchants from local up to national level are examples of this activity.
- ATMs ('hole in the wall cash dispensers') as operated by banking groups such as Link, where demand for cash varies considerably but dispensers rarely run out.

Forecasting future demand

Before any inventory control system can be planned and subsequently established, it is necessary to have an estimate of future demand. For instance, the demand for bread for a small group of students living in a flat is an order of magnitude less than that for a Hall of Residence providing meals for several hundred students. Hence, the type and size of the inventory control operation run to meet that latter demand will be totally different to that operated by the students occupying the flat. Since forecasting is a necessary precursor to designing any inventory control system, this topic will be dealt with in detail in Chapter 8.

Inventory control – policies

To run a successful inventory system, which should effectively control the supply of replenishment orders (placed by the stock-holder on his/her suppliers) against the requirements of demand orders (placed by customers of the inventory system) it is clearly necessary to have a policy which defines a series of rules as to how replenishment orders are to be raised. In an inventory control environment, the two most important rules which need to be defined are:

- How or when are orders for replenishment triggered, which can be arranged to occur either:
  - at that time when stock-on-hand (the physical stock held plus any outstanding replenishment orders less committed stock) reaches a certain level, or
  - on a regular time basis, for instance once a month, once a quarter.
- When a replenishment order is triggered the size of the replenishment order can be:
  - set at a relatively fixed value, or,
  - calculated as a variable value, in sympathy with the inventory situation existing at the time the replenishment order is raised.

The two main inventory policies used in practice are the re-order level policy and re-order cycle policy.

The re-order level policy

The two principal rules controlling a re-order level policy are:

1. When the inventory held or stock-on-hand falls to or below a pre-specified level, an order for replenishment is raised immediately, and
2. Because, in this policy the level of inventory held at the time a replenishment order is raised is at or just below the pre-specified re-order level, stock balances are best maintained with a relatively fixed replenishment order size (often the 'Economic Order Quantity').

Taking the group of students living in a flat as an example, on the assumption that the demand for bread has been estimated or forecast at one loaf per day, a feasible inventory policy that could be operated by the students would be to use one loaf as the re-order level and to purchase a fresh loaf the moment supplies of bread fell below the one loaf level and, to minimize the students' immediate cash outlay, the replenishment order could be a single loaf which would produce stock balances as shown in Figure 7.1.

Given that the students' flat was located reasonably near to local shops, in practice there would be no delay between the realization that a fresh loaf of bread needed to be purchased and the actual purchase. In a more realistic inventory control situation, however, there is always a delay (known as the lead-time) between the raising of an order and its subsequent delivery. It should be noted that, in this example, for the re-order level to be successfully implemented it is necessary that a replenishment order can be raised at any point in time. Such a system, therefore, requires continuous monitoring of the level of inventory held, which in this example might be feasible for students who can go to the local shops at any time but would not be feasible for an over-worked lecturer whose only free day to go shopping is Saturday – a situation more suited to a re-order cycle policy!

The re-order cycle policy

The two principal rules controlling a re-order cycle policy are:

1. Replenishments orders are raised at regular intervals of time, say

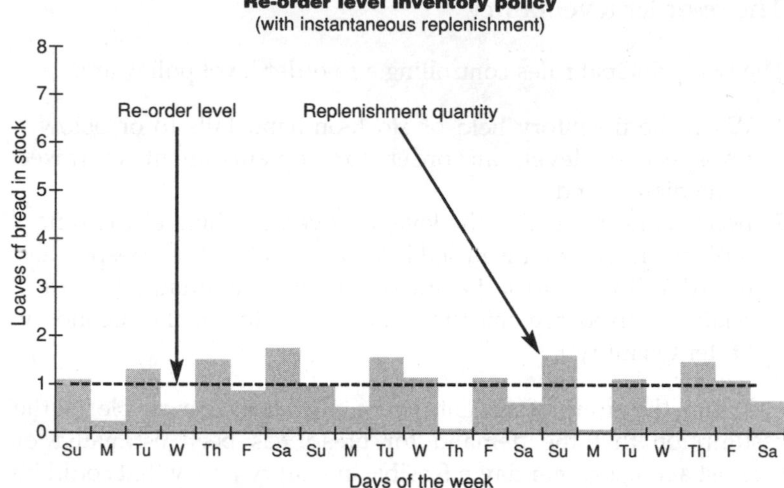

Figure 7.1 Re-order level policy stock balances with re-order level of one loaf and replenishment quantity of one loaf

weekly, monthly, quarterly and so on, the period between these intervals being defined as the *review period*, and

2. When a replenishment order is raised on a regular time basis, it is clear that the inventory held (or stock-on-hand) could be at virtually any level, either relatively high (if demand since the previous replenishment hand been lower than usual) or relatively low (if demand since the previous replenishment had been higher than usual). To overcome this problem, therefore, the size of the replenishment quantity in this policy is calculated as the difference between a nominal maximum stock level and the current inventory held. This helps balance the overall system as a large replenishment order is placed when the inventory held at the time the replenishment order is raised is low, and conversely a small replenishment order is placed if the inventory held is relatively high.

As an example of this policy one could visualize that for an overworked lecturer, who can only get to the shops on Saturdays, the re-order cycle policy would be the natural, and more appropriate policy for replenishing stocks of bread. The review period in this situation is clearly a week, and prior to going to the shops the lecturer would need to check the number of loaves held in stock (presumably in a deep freeze). Assuming the demand for bread in the lecturer's household was the same as the students in the flat (that is, one loaf a day), the replenishment policy which would then need to be operated would be for the lecturer to purchase enough loaves to bring stocks up to the nominal maximum of seven (based on a loaf a day for the seven days of the week), producing stock balances as shown in Figure 7.2..

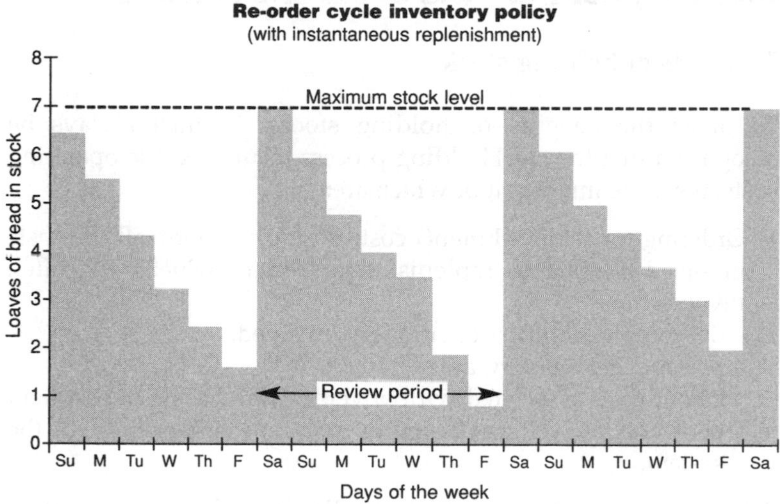

Figure 7.2 Re-order cycle policy stock balances with weekly review period and maximum stock level of seven loaves

Comparisons of the re-order level and re-order cycle inventory polices

Because technically the re-order level policy requires a continuous review of stocks held it tends to hold much lower stocks than the re-order cycle policy, as can be clearly seen in the students' flat bread situation compared with the lecturer's household. However, this continuous review clearly can mean that the cost of replenishment for the re-order level policy is relatively high compared with the re-order cycle policy, where replenishments are made on a regular basis and, as a result, can be better planned. This higher cost of continuous review could perhaps be equated by the students against the opportunity cost of taking on a part-time job which would prevent them getting to shops during the week! In a more realistic situation, the re-order cycle policy allows the stockholder to arrange that replenishment orders for many items available from a single supplier can all be made at the same time on a single order, thus reducing replenishment costs considerably compared with the re-order level policy where in the worst scenario all replenishment orders could be for a single item.

Inventory control – the costs and benefits

The costs of holding stock

To offset the benefits of holding stocks, it must always be recognized that the stockholding process incurs specific operating costs, the more important of which are:

- Ordering (or replenishment) costs – which include all the costs involved in raising replenishment orders which will often involve:
  - the complex multipart stationery involved;
  - postage and delivery, and
  - labour costs associated with buyers or purchasing department personnel as well as *chasing* or *expediting* orders through the system.

All of these can be reduced drastically through computerization and the use of EDI (Electronic Data Interchange) but are never negligible.

- Storage (or holding) costs – which are generally expressed as a percentage of the unit cost of the item involved (typically from 20 to 30 per cent p.a.) and made up of:
  - the costs of borrowing money to invest in stock or alternatively the loss of possible interest that could have been made had a company not used its own money to invest in stock (typically from 8 to 15 per cent p.a.);
  - the costs directly associated with storing goods, that is, storemen's wages, rates, heating and lighting, store's transport, racking and pallatization, protective clothing, weighing equipment and so on;
  - costs involved in preventing deterioration of stock (typically from 0 to 30 per cent per annum);
  - costs incurred as a result of obsolescence which could include costs of re-work or scrapping (typically from 4 to 7 per cent p.a.);

  - costs of insurance to cover fire, theft and third party injury. (typically about 1.5 per cent p.a.).

- Stockout costs – costs which are incurred as a result of not being able to satisfy customer demand because stocks are not immediately available. These costs are generally very difficult to define in terms of whether they should be assessed on a basis of the actual number of units of shortage or the time period over which the shortage occurs. In view of this difficulty, most inventory control models ignore stockout costs and argue that they are provided for, if somewhat obliquely, by offering a reasonable level of service to customers of the inventory system.
- Administration costs – which can cover a multitude of fixed costs which are only incurred because stocks are held, computing costs for instance.

All the costs mentioned above are difficult to estimate with any accuracy and elements of some are regarded by many companies and organizations as 'general overheads', not directly associated with the costs of holding stocks or inventories. Hence, inventory control should not be regarded as an exact science.

The benefits of holding stock

To be viable, the holding of inventory (or stocks) must offer benefits to the customers whose demand requirements are met by the stockholding process. Some of the principal benefits of holding stock are:

- The demands of customers are buffered by the stockholding process from the suppliers of replenishment orders to that stockholding process. Thus, given the holding of stock is organized economically, the frequent small demand orders of customers can be met more effectively by the supply of large, infrequent replenishment orders by suppliers. Thus stock can often act as an effective cushion against interruptions to supply. Although not immediately thought of in terms of an item controlled by orthodox inventory control procedures, stocks of drinking water facilitated by the construction of reservoirs clearly assists in the process of meeting customers' demand throughout the year, even though the supply of water through natural rainfall is partially interrupted during the summer months.

- Because inventory systems are replenished with relatively large orders, the unit costs of the items provisioned by such large orders can often be reduced due to:
  - longer production runs absorbing set-up costs more effectively;
  - discounts or price breaks offered for large orders;
  - more economical transport and packaging costs.

Conclusion

Inventory control can be regarded as the science-based art of controlling the amount of inventory (or stock) held, in various forms, within a business or organization to meet the demands placed upon that business or organization at a cost which is not prohibitive to the stockholder.

Before any inventory control system can be planned, it is necessary to have an estimate of the future demand that the system is going to be exposed to. This is usually achieved using a forecasting system.

Any inventory control system needs to be controlled by policies based on a series of rules which define:

- When and how replenishment orders placed by the stockholder on his/her suppliers are triggered, and
- What size replenishment orders are placed when that triggering occurs.

The two most commonly used inventory policies are:

- The re-order level policy within which a replenishment order for a relatively fixed sized quantity is triggered when stocks fall to or below a pre-specified re-order level, and
- The re-order cycle policy within which replenishment orders are placed at regular intervals of time and are of a size which if there were no delay, would bring stock back up to a pre-specified, maximum level.

The holding of inventory (or stock) offers benefits to the customer which ultimately have to be paid for to offset the costs of holding stock incurred by the stockholder. Clearly in a successfully designed stock control system the benefits should outweigh the costs and this can only occur when a balance between the two extremes of over or under-stocking has been achieved.

8 Demand Forecasting and Inventory Control

FORECASTING is a necessary pre-requisite to all inventory control situations. Without an estimate of the future customer demand it is impossible to plan the levels of inventories (or stocks) that will be required to offer customers a reasonable level of service.

Forecasting versus prediction

In general terms, forecasting at all levels from long term to short term can be interpreted as being a deterministic process of estimating a future event by casting forward past data. In all these forecasting processes, past data are initially analysed to establish the basic level of demand (the stationary element) and any underlying trends (such as growth and seasonality) which characterize the data. This information is then used in a pre-determined way (such as using formulae) to obtain an estimate of the future. Thus forecasting processes are usually largely automated (that is, calculated with computer programs). Prediction, however, is generally interpreted as a process of estimating a future event based primarily on subjective considerations and is, therefore, not automated but based on manual methods.

In practice an automatically produced forecast, calculated on assumptions that characteristic trends identified in past demand data will continue into the future, should always be open to alteration if predictions, such as changes in market conditions, appear to suggest that such assumptions could be invalid. Many years ago, the sudden introduction of VAT on double glazed products depressed the market for several months such that forecasts based on the pre-VAT era clearly became invalid for a period of time until the market readjusted and restabilized.

However, because predictions are predominantly subjective and involve manual interruption, they are generally far more expensive to implement on a routine basis than forecasts. Therefore, where many product lines or services are involved, it is generally more effective to operate on the assumption that scientifically produced forecasts are assumed to be satisfactory unless and until a monitoring procedure indicates that the forecast for a particular product line or service is no longer in control; at which time predictions of future demand may well be required to re-establish the validity of the forecast. Fortunately very effective monitoring systems are available to control forecasts and these are discussed in Chapter 9.

Different types of forecasting methods

A useful way of classifying or categorizing demand forecasting methods is to define the type of forecast on the basis of the *time period* associated with the demand data which are being analysed, as illustrated in Table 8.1.

Table 8.1 Categorization of type of demand forecast based on the underlying time unit of data involved

Category or Type of Demand Forecast	*Time Period Associated with the Data being Analysed*	*Example of Forecasting Application*	*Forecasting Techniques Used*
Immediate term	1/4 day to 1 day	Electricity demand forecasting	Various
Short term	1 week to 1 month	Demand forecasting in industry and commerce	Simple exponentially weighted averages and derivatives for growth and seasonal trends
Medium term	1 month to 1 year	Sales and financial forecasting	Regression, curve fitting, time series analysis
		Econometric forecasting	Multi parameter models
Long term	1 year to 1 decade	Technological forecasting	DELPHI, think tanks and similar

Short-term forecasting

Although there is no strict demarcation between the various types of forecasting categorized within Table 8.1, it is generally assumed that short-term forecasting methods, at the *cheap and cheerful* end of the forecasting spectrum, are most suitable in situations where there are many components, product lines or services as typically does occur in an inventory control environment. Also, within an inventory environment, it is often true that the demand patterns being analysed are relatively *fast moving*, with an average per period in excess of twenty, such that the normal probability distribution can be assumed to represent the distribution of demand per unit of time. The forecasting models used when operating in such an environment are therefore necessarily required to be simple and relatively cheap to operate while still being robust. The family of forecasting models based on the *exponentially weighted average* has proved to meet these criteria more satisfactorily than any other group of models and has traditionally become the basis for forecasting in many inventory control situations because of its:

- Computational cheapness in terms of processing time and storage requirements;
- Robustness and ability for the forecasting process to be monitored so that 'out of control' situations can be readily detected;
- Ease of 'starting up' when initializing new items with no previous demand history;
- Adaptability in terms of changing sensitivity in line with the characteristic of the demand data encountered, and
- Flexibility in terms of ability to cope with stationary, growth and seasonal demand patterns.

Characteristics of customer demand patterns requiring forecasting

Inventory control systems are required to cope with a variety of different customer demand patterns for which forecasts are necessary if an effective overall policy for controlling inventory (or stocks) is to be achieved. In practice, in ascending order of complexity, it is assumed that the following demand patterns can exist:

1. Stationary demand

This assumes that although customer demand per unit time fluctuates, there is no apparent underlying growth or seasonal trend. Figure 8.1 illustrates the basic stationary character of such data but also identifies the fact that variability in demand exists. Because no growth or seasonality are assumed in stationary demand patterns, forecasts ahead are fixed in value and the forecast for one period ahead is the forecast for any number of periods ahead. An example of stationary demand is door furniture (handles, knobs and so on) which past analysis has been shown to remain very stable over the years and, surprisingly, is not overly influenced by seasonal patterns.

Although within a stationary demand pattern no growth or seasonality is assumed to exist, it should be accepted that occasionally fundamental changes in the demand pattern may occur, but these are presumed to be short-term in nature, such as:

- *Impulses* – individual demands which are significantly higher or lower than normal. Such impulses are best ignored by a forecasting system linked to an inventory control policy, since such policies are basically designed to cope with a reasonably stable level of demand with a known, measurable degree of variation. There are many examples of 'one-off' demands that effectively represent an impulse; the sudden surge in demand to buy petrol prior to a budget being a prime example.
- *Step changes* – a series of successive demands which are significantly higher or lower than normal which in effect produces two stationary demand situations – one before the step change followed by another stationary situation at a different level subsequent to the step change. The ideal response of a forecast to a step change in demand is that it should react as quickly as possible in adapting to the post step change level of demand. Should this not be feasible, a competent forecasting system should at least identify that such a step change has occurred and should also instigate remedial action to ensure that the forecast, which will naturally lag behind such a sudden change of level, is corrected. An example of a step increase in demand could be exhibited when a competitor ceases to trade and that competitor's demand is distributed amongst alternative suppliers/stock holders. Unlike an impulse, a step change is sustained beyond the period of the initial increase (or decrease) in demand.

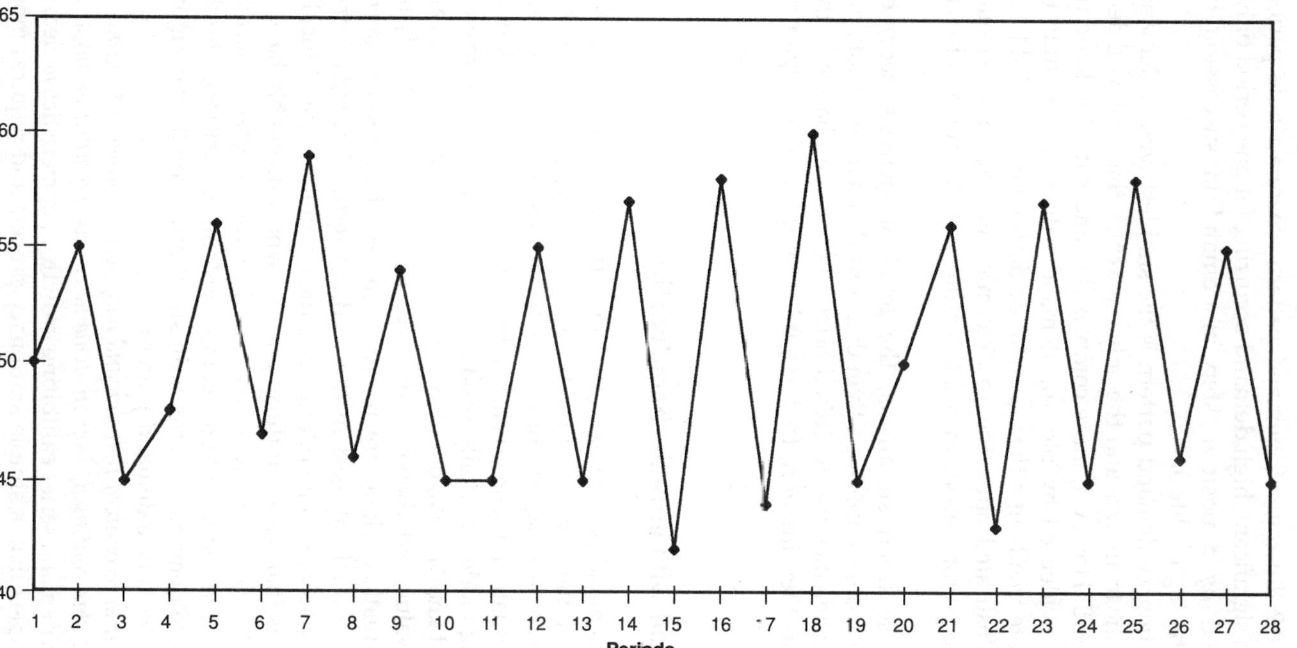

Figure 8.1 Stationary demand pattern (with no long-term growth or seasonality)

Figure 8.2 illustrates a demand pattern where a single period impulse (a significant, high demand occurring for one period only) is followed by a positive step in demand (a succession of significantly high values).

The stationary demand pattern is the simplest type of demand characteristic to analyse and the only one which this book will deal with in detail. However, more complex demand patterns do occur as can be evidenced by plotting demand values against time to demonstrate trends in either growth (or decline) or seasonality. A more sophisticated approach to determine growth and seasonal trends is to perform an *autocorrelation analysis* as described in Lewis (1997).

For these trend situations, the level of analysis becomes somewhat more complicated than that considered in this book, but their characteristics are described briefly here to emphasize to the reader that other situations to the simple stationary demand pattern do exist.

2. Demand with growth characteristics

Where a demand pattern exhibits a growth characteristic over the longer term, the forecasting models required to accommodate that growth become more complex than those used in the stationary demand situation discussed earlier. In growth situations, stationary forecasting models not only produce forecasts which in retrospect lag behind known data, but also produce forecasts ahead which are fixed in value and therefore do not respond to the underlying growth situation. There are many examples of demand patterns exhibiting growth, at least in the medium term. Currently (early 2000) the sales of mobile phones and the resulting demand for the components that make up those phones (which inevitably have to be stocked somewhere), together with the support services needed to operate the mobile phone companies' infrastructures, should demonstrate demand patterns with significant growth and Figure 8.3 illustrates such a demand pattern.

(Note: *It is recognized that demand may decline rather than grow, in which case this continual drop in demand can be regarded as negative growth*). A demand series exhibiting growth characteristics is clearly more complex than a simple stationary process and requires more complex forecasting models to:

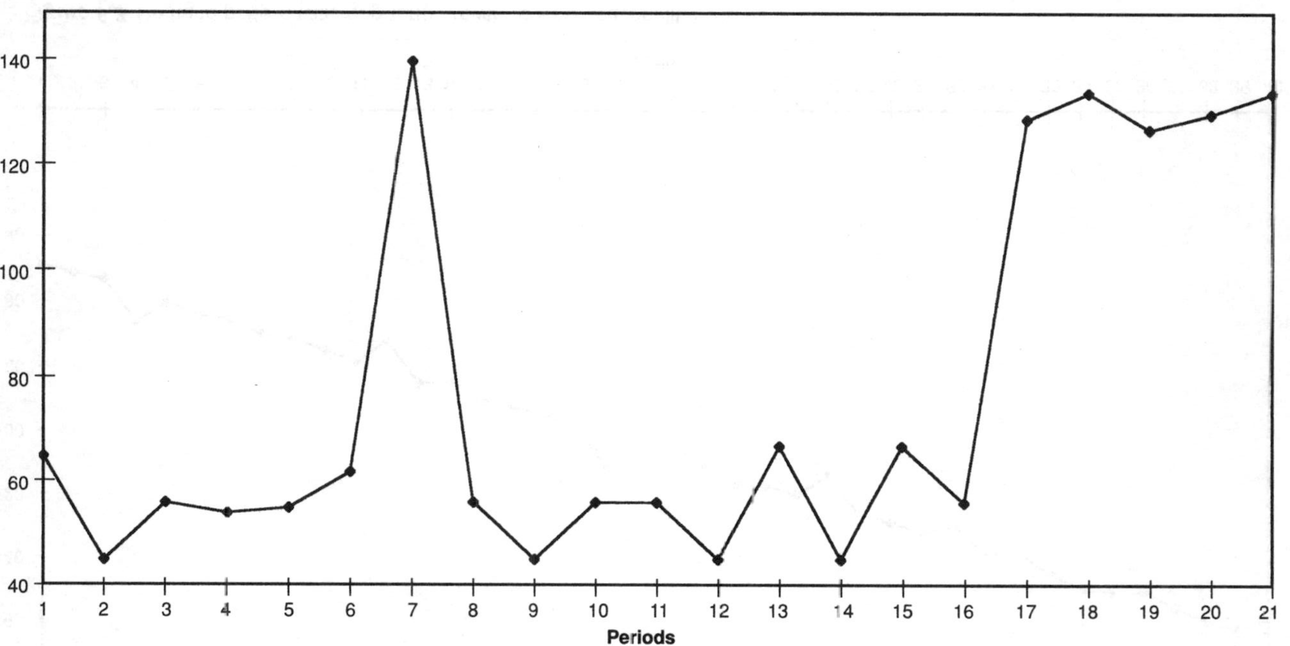

Figure 8.2 Stationary demand pattern (including an impulse followed by a step)

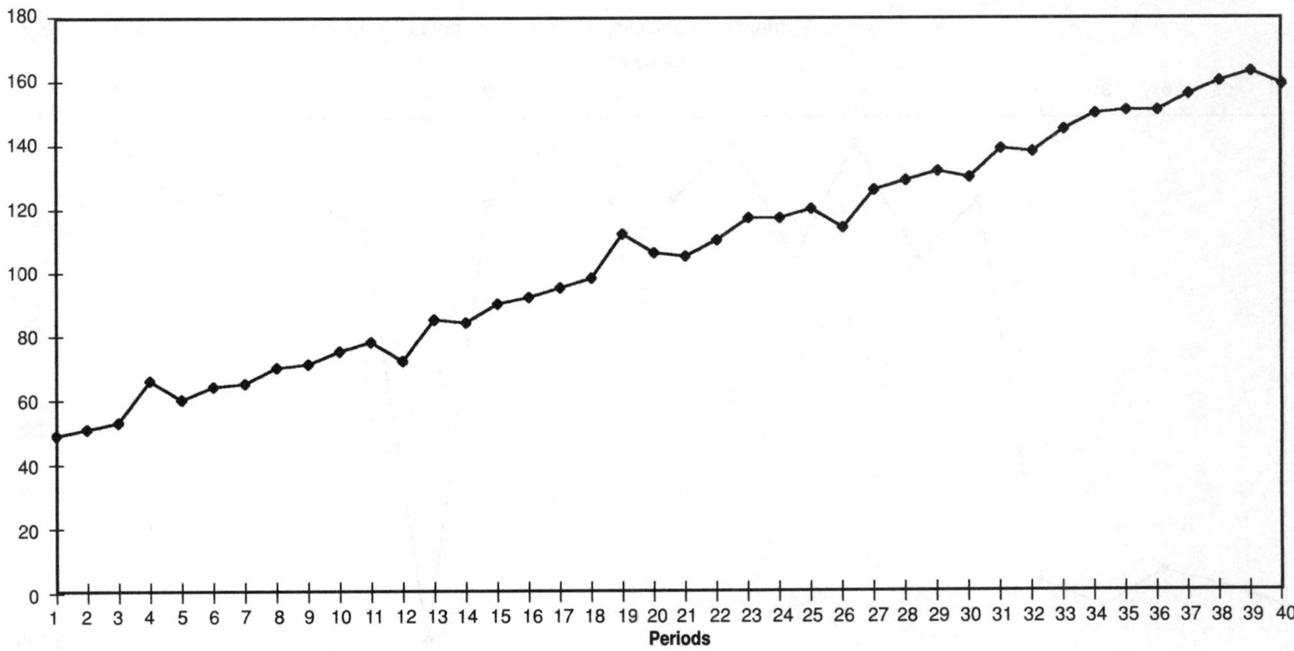

Figure 8.3 Demand pattern with long-term growth (but no seasonality)

- Identify the rate of growth (or decline) of the demand data, and
- Incorporate the rate of growth (or decline) in the forecasts.

The description of forecasting models to cope with demand with growth characteristics are beyond the scope of this half-book, but the method referred to as *double smoothing* by Brown (1962) has proved popular for inventory control situations and is fully described in Lewis (1997).

3. Demand with seasonal characteristics

Many demand series are influenced by the seasons of the year and by other events which occur annually. In such situations it is possible to establish the degree to which demand in any particular period of the year (such as month, quarter or accounting period) is higher or lower than for a typical average period. Hence the aim of forecasting models taking seasonality into account is to establish this relationship for each and every period within the year and to use the de-seasonalizing factors that are identified by this process to produce forecasts. For technical reasons it is generally assumed that growth may also exist in demand patterns characterized by seasonality as is shown in Figure 8.4. If there is no growth, the analysis simply registers actual growth as negligible. An excellent example of seasonal demand is represented by the demand on local food shops in residential districts occupied mainly by students. Again the description of forecasting models to cope with demand having seasonal characteristics is beyond the scope of this half-book, but of those which have been developed the method based on either additive or multiplicative seasonal factors by Holt (1957) has proved popular for inventory control situations and is fully described in Lewis (1997).

4. Forecasting in stationary (no growth or seasonality) situations

As has been argued earlier in this chapter, the simplest demand environment within which to produce forecasts occurs when it can be assumed that the underlying demand process is stationary. The basic assumption within a stationary demand process is that there is variation about a relatively stationary average value and that any change in the average value (such as a step upwards or downwards) is due to a special, one-off cause rather than to overall growth or seasonality.

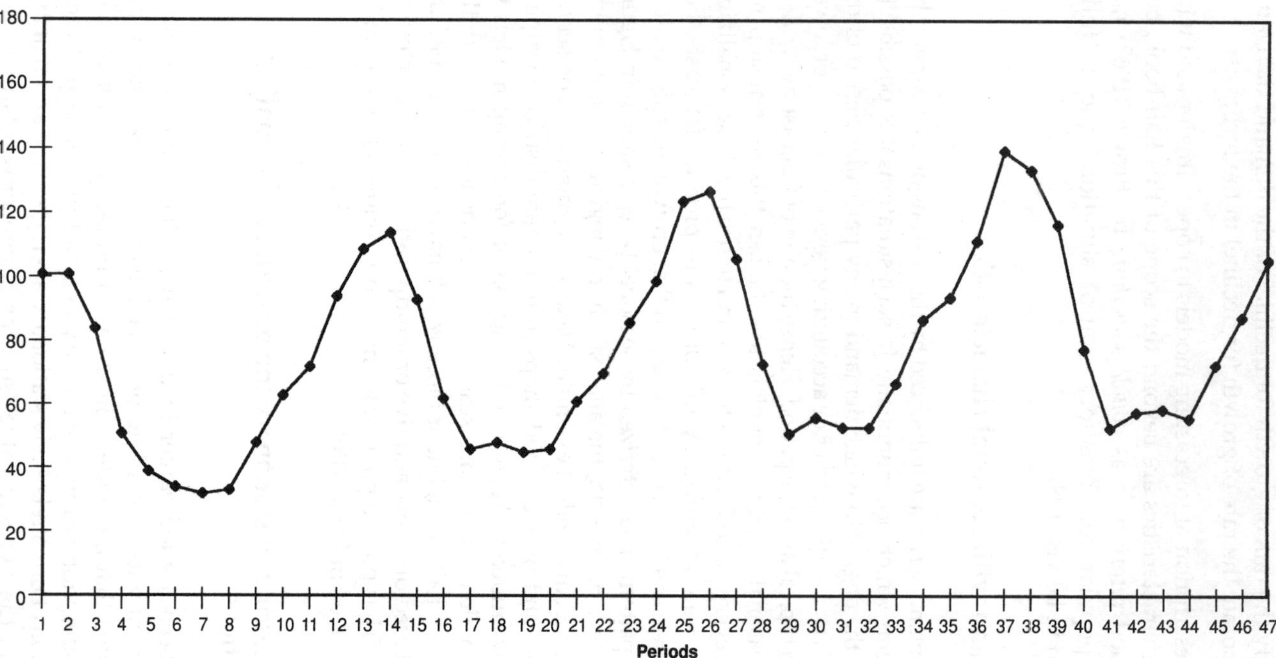

Figure 8.4 Seasonal demand pattern including four seasons (based on monthly data) with an element of long-term growth

Relating forecast and demand data to time periods

Before developing specific forecasting models to be linked with inventory control policies, it is clear that in all forecasting situations it is necessary to define the timing of both forecasts and demand data to the particular time period to which they belong or relate. The convention adopted is to regard the current period (that is, now) as present time t and refer all other timings to present time. In practice, therefore, d_t defines the demand that occurred in the most recent period under consideration.

Past time is considered as negative with respect to the current period t, hence d_{t-1} defines the demand that occurred in the period immediately previous to the period in which d_t occurred.

Although demand data can only occur in the past, forecast are clearly targeted to the future. Hence, future time is defined as positive with respect to the current period and f_{t+1} would define the timing of the forecast for the next period, that is, the period following the current period.

For the situation depicted in Table 8.2, assuming that the demand value has just been collected for the month of March, and that a forecast is required for April, the following timings would apply.

Table 8.2 Relationship between periods (months) and subscript *t*

Month	**January**	**February** Previous period	**March** Current period	**April** Next period
Time period	$(t-2)$	$(t-1)$	(t)	$(t+1)$
Data	40	44	36	?
Forecast				40

In a stationary demand situation, because no growth or seasonality is assumed, the forecast for one period ahead is the forecast for any number of T periods ahead, where T is any specified forecast horizon projecting into the future. Hence, in the stationary demand situation *only* the forecast for T periods ahead f_{t+T} is given by:

$$f_{t+T} = f_{t+1}$$

The 'moving average' as a forecasting model

Referring to Table 8.2, the forecast of 40 for next month (April) f_{t+1} based on a 'moving average' m_t calculated this month (March, that is, now at time t) could be evaluated as:

$$f_{t+1} = m_t = (1/3)d_t + (1/3)d_{t-1} + (1/3)d_{t-2} = (1/3)36 + (1/3)44 + (1/3)40 = 40$$

The more general form of the *moving average* as a forecasting model would be:

$$f_{t+1} = m_t = (1/n)d_t + (1/n)d_{t-1} + \ldots (1/n)d_{t-n+1} \qquad (8.1)$$

where $n = 2,3$...........12 and so on, and where the sum of the n weights of $1/n$ will always sum to one, *this being the definition of a true average.*

However, in practice, the use of a moving average as a forecasting model poses the following significant, practical problems:

- It is difficult to initialize, that is, to start from a situation where no data exist.
- It requires relatively large amounts of data to be stored (for example if a 12-period moving average is to be operated, 11 periods of demand values would need to be stored until the twelfth period's value becomes available to complete the calculation as defined by Equation 8.1). This represents a significant data storage problem if forecasts are to be provided for several thousand stocked items.
- It imposes difficulties in changing sensitivity in that the number of periods included within the average would need to be varied.
- It imposes a sudden cut off in weighting for data not included, that is, with a 12-period moving average the demand value related to the period just excluded from the average contributes absolutely nothing to that average whereas the previous period's value (only one period younger) contributes $1/12$ or 8.33 per cent.
- It weights all data equally irrespective of their age; whereas simple logic would suggest that more recent data should be weighted more heavily than older data.

The final problem of *equal weighting* could be overcome by developing an one-period ahead forecast based on an unequally weighted moving average, such as:

$$f_{t+1} = m_t = (0.5)d_t + (0.3)d_{t-1} + (0.2)d_{t-2}$$

which is a valid, average based forecasting model since the sum of the weights do indeed add up to one.

It is the extension of this concept of an unequally weighted moving average which leads to the development of an average with an infinite number of weights which decrease exponentially with time, that is, an exponentially weighted average.

The exponentially weighted average as a forecasting model

The definition of an average u_t with weights declining exponentially with time would be of the general form of an infinite series defined as:

$$u_t = \alpha d_t + \alpha(1-\alpha)d_{t-1} + \alpha(1-\alpha)^2 d_{t-2} + \alpha(1-\alpha)^3 d_{t-3} + \alpha(1-\alpha)^4 d_{t-4} \ldots \quad (8.2)$$

where α is a constant whose value must be between zero and one, since to produce a true average the sum of weights must sum to one (at infinity). A value of $\alpha = 0.2$ is a good compromise figure and would produce the following weighting series:

$$\alpha + \alpha(1-\alpha) + \alpha(1-\alpha)^2 + \alpha(1-\alpha)^3 + \alpha(1-\alpha)^4 + \alpha(1-\alpha)^5 \ldots$$

and so on;

$$0.2 + 0.16 + 0.128 + 0.1024 + 0.08192 + 0.06554 + 0.052429 \ldots$$

and so on;

which with only 7 weights already sums to 0.79, with 20 weights sums to 0.991, with 33 weights sums to 0.999 and theoretically will sum to one at infinity.

On first examination, a forecast based on Equation 8.2 would appear to be relatively complicated to implement and with an infinite number of demand values. This approach would not appear to solve the problem of the amount of data that has to be stored (already referred to as a major disadvantage of the moving average). However, it is possible (see the end of this chapter for a detailed development of this form of the exponentially weighted average) to show that Equation 8.2 can be modified to a much simpler statement such that a one-period ahead forecast f_{t+1} can be shown to be of the form:

$$f_{t+1} = u_t = \alpha d_t + (1-\alpha)u_{t-1} \tag{8.3}$$

where $$u_{t-1} = \alpha d_{t-1} + \alpha(1-\alpha)d_{t-2} \ldots$$

which is the equivalent of

$$f_{t+1} = u_t = u_{t-1} + \alpha(d_t - u_{t-1})$$

and since the current forecasting error e_t can be defined as the current demand value d_t minus the one-period ahead forecast evaluated last period u_{t-1}, then

$$e_t = d_t - u_{t-1}$$

and therefore

$$f_{t+1} = u_t = u_{t-1} + \alpha e_t \tag{8.4}$$

which can easily be interpreted, for those not too comfortable with simple algebra, as:

NEW FORECAST = OLD FORECAST + ALPHA × CURRENT FORECASTING ERROR.

Advantages of the simple exponentially weighted average

In contrast to the moving average, the *simple* exponentially weighted average offers the following advantages:

- It is easy to initialize, since once an estimate for u_{t-1} (the previous period's forecast) is made, forecasting can proceed (given that a value for α is also decided) since all the unknowns on the right-hand side of Equation 8.3 are then defined.
- It is economical in data storage terms since u_{t-1} embodies all previous data (that is, $u_{t-1} = \alpha d_{t-1} + \alpha(1-\alpha)d_{t-2}$..) and hence only the value of u_{t-1} needs to be retained from one period to the next.
- It is capable of having its sensitivity changed at any time by altering the value of α (the exponential smoothing constant) just as long as the value of α is set between zero and one, and
- It does not produce a sudden cut-off in weighting of demand

data irrespective of age. Even data 20 periods old are theoretically weighted with $\alpha(1-\alpha)^{20}$ which, although a very small value, is certainly not zero.

The calculations required to produce a forecasting schedule based on a simple exponentially weighted average with alpha $\alpha = 0.2$, for the demand pattern originally shown as Figure 8.2, are shown in the first four rows of Table 8.3. In detail, the calculations involved are as follows:

- Row 1: the current period's demand values d_t are displayed. Clearly at the end of the first January (initially regarded as the current period *t*) only the value of 55 is known;
- Row 2: the current period's forecast is normally the one period ahead forecast from the previous period, but the 50 for January has to be an initial prediction (based on subjective judgement) as to what the demand is likely to be since no previous data are available;
- Row 3: the current period's error is calculated simply as the current period's demand 55 minus the current period's forecast 50;
- Row 4: the one period ahead forecast is established initially as $f_{t+1} = 0.2 \times 55 + (1 - 0.2) \times 50$, which becomes 51. This value is then carried forward to February's Row 1 (as indicated by the arrow), and
- February then becomes the current period *t* and at the end of February, when the demand value of 50 is recorded, the sequence of calculations is repeated.

(Note: Since in most inventory situations one is dealing with individual items, where the value of the forecast does not produce a whole number, it is usual to round to the nearest whole number by adding 0.5 and then take the integer value, for example 6.2 + 0.5 = 6.7 which rounds to 6 whereas 6.7 + 0.5 = 7.2 which rounds to 7).

The response of the one month ahead forecast, as calculated in Table 8.3, for demand data which contains an impulse followed by a positive step, is shown in Figure 8.5.

Examining the response of this *simple* exponentially weighted average forecast, it should be noted that:

- For the first four months, during which the demand is fairly stable, as would be expected the forecast falls within the overall envelope of the demand values.

Table 8.3 Forecasting schedule based on a simple exponentially weighted average $\alpha = 0.2$

		Jan	Feb	Mar	Apr	May	Jun	Jul	Aug	Sep	Oct	Nov	Dec	Jan
1	**This month's demand** d_t	55	50	58	49	86	52	54	49	58	68			
2	**Last month's forecast** $f_t = u_{t-1}$	50*	51	51	52	51	58	57	56	55	56	58	58	58
3	**This month's forecast error** $e_t = d_t - f_t$	5	–1	7	–3	35	–6	–3	–7	3	12			
4	**One month ahead forecast** $f_{t+1} = u_t = \alpha\, d_t + (1-\alpha)u_{t-1}$	51	51	52	51	58	57	56	55	56	58			
5	**Squared Error** e_t^2	25	1	49	9	1225	36	9	49	9	144		**MSE**	147
6	**Absolute Percentage Error** APE = $100\|e_t\|/d_t$	9%	2%	12%	6%	41%	12%	6%	14%	5%	18%		**MAPE**	12%
7	**Smoothed error** $\bar{e}_t = 0.2e_t + (1-0.2)\bar{e}_{t-1}$	1.0#	0.6	1.9	0.9	7.7	5.0	3.4	1.3	1.6	3.7			
8	**Mean Absolute Deviation** $MAD_t = 0.2\|e_t\| + (1-0.2)\, MAD_{t-1}$	5.0##	4.2	4.8	4.4	10.5	9.6	8.3	8.0	7.0	8.0			
9	**Tracking signal** $T_t = \bar{e}_t/MAD_t$	0.2	0.1	0.4	0.2	0.7	0.5	0.4	0.2	0.2	0.5			

* Initial prediction   # $\bar{e}_{t-1} = 0$ ## $MAD_{t-1} = 0.1 * u_{t-1}$

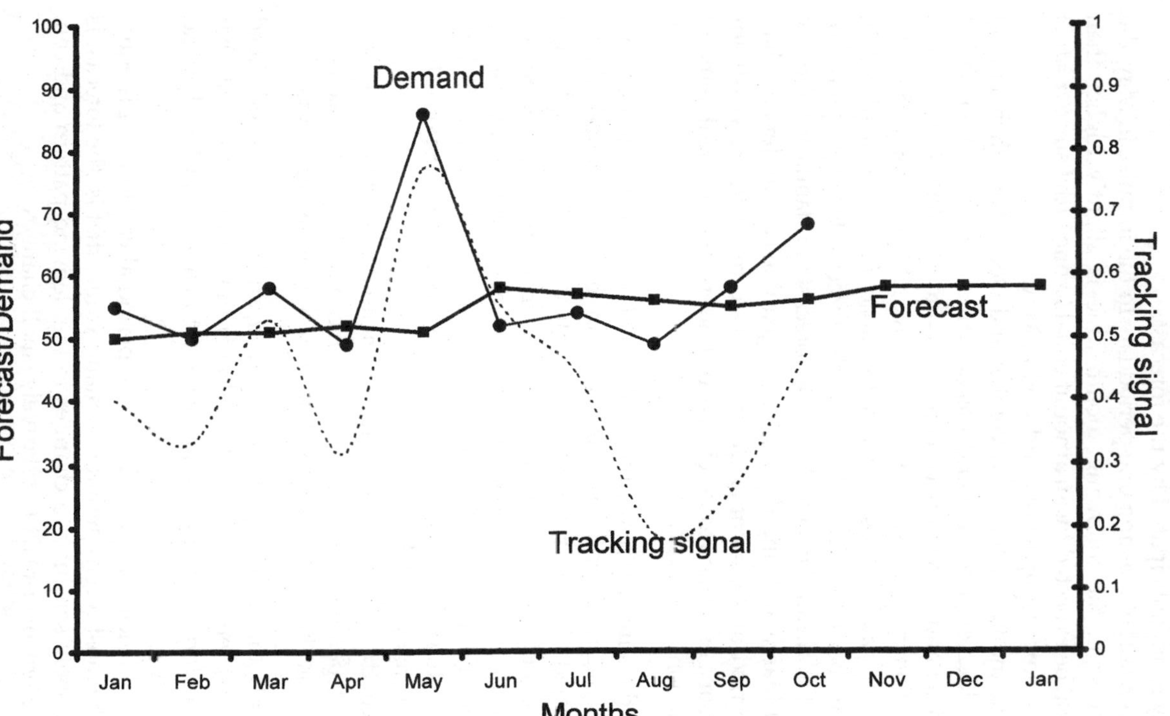

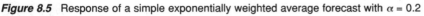

Figure 8.5 Response of a simple exponentially weighted average forecast with $\alpha = 0.2$

- The impulse (one individual, large demand value) occurring in May is not anticipated by the forecast.
- As a result of reacting one period late to the impulse in May, the forecast in the following month June is slightly higher than might be expected by an amount equal to one fifth (since $\alpha = 0.2$) of the forecasting error produced in May.
- In the months October, November and December, where clearly a sudden spurt in demand has occurred, the forecast has failed to react and, in retrospect, can be seen to lag behind. Also, since a stationary forecast assumes no growth beyond the end of the known data, the last one-month ahead forecast (calculated in December for January) becomes the forecast for any number of months ahead. This results in the forecasts for January, February and March all being the same. If a genuine step in demand had occurred in the months October to December, the forecasts for January to March would clearly be understating the real demand situation.

For the simple exponentially weighted average, when the value of α is high, a good response to a an upward change can be anticipated. However, with such a high value of α a single high demand value (impulse) can cause an over-reaction one period late (that is, the forecast is so sensitive it can over-react to any *noise* in the demand process). Conversely, when the value of α is low, although the effect of an impulse will be ignored, the response to an upward change will be poor.

Since the sensitivity of an exponentially weighted average clearly depends on the value of α which can only vary between zero and one, at the two extreme values of α the following occurs:

- If $\alpha = 0$, then from Equation 8.3 $f_{t+1} = u_t$ and the one-period ahead forecast remains fixed at the value of the previous forecast, that is, the forecast is totally insensitive to changes in the demand pattern, or
- If $\alpha = 1$, then $f_{t+1} = d_t$ and the one-period ahead forecast is equal to the most recent period's demand value, that is, the forecast is extremely sensitive to changes in the demand pattern and can, therefore, over-react to relatively small changes.

Ideally the *best* value of α a will be that which minimizes the sum of squared forecasting errors, but in the majority of practical situations values of either 0.1 or 0.2 are useful compromise figures.

Conclusion

The *simple* exponentially weighted average represents an ideal forecasting model for producing relatively short-term forecasts for inventory control systems when demand is stationary. Its advantages are that it is:

- Easy to start up for new products;
- Economical in data storage terms;
- Easily modified in terms of sensitivity of response;
- Generally robust.

However, when more complex demand patterns exist, such as those influenced by growth or seasonality, adaptations of the *simple* exponentially weighted average forecasting model are required. For instance, Brown's *double smoothed* model has been used traditionally to cope with growth and Holt's model for growth combined with seasonality. Both these more complicated models are beyond the scope of this book but are covered in Lewis (1997).

Proof to show that a forecast based on a simple exponentially weighted average can be simplified to the statement that:

NEW FORECAST = OLD FORECAST + ALPHA × CURRENT FORECASTING ERROR.

If:

$$u_t = \alpha d_t + \alpha(1-\alpha)d_{t-1} + \alpha(1-\alpha)^2 d_{t-2} \ldots$$

then

$$u_t = \alpha d_t + (1-\alpha)[\ \alpha d_{t-1} + \alpha(1-\alpha)d_{t-2} \ldots$$

and since

$$[\alpha d_{t-1} + \alpha(1-\alpha)d_{t-2} \ldots = u_{t-1}$$

it follows that

$$u_t = \alpha d_t + (1-\alpha)u_{t-1}$$

or

$$u_t = u_{t-1} + \alpha(d_t - u_{t-1})$$

and since

$d_t - u_{t-1} = e_t$ that is, the current forecasting error.

Hence it follows for stationary demand situations where it is assumed that the forecast for one period ahead is the same for all periods ahead (that is, there is no growth or seasonality) then:

$$f_{t+T} = f_{t+1} = u_t = u_{t-1} + \alpha e_t$$

or in words

NEW FORECAST = OLD FORECAST + ALPHA × CURRENT FORECASTING ERROR.

Question

1. Complete the forecasting schedule shown below based on a value of $\alpha = 0.2$. Round to the nearest integer value.

		Jan	Feb	Mar	Apr	May	Jun
1	**Current period's demand** d_t	123	100	178	122		
2	**Current period's forecast** $f_t = u_{t-1}$	100					
3	**Current period's forecast error** $e_t = d_t - f_t$						
4	**One period ahead forecast** $f_{t+1} = u_t = \alpha d_t + (1 - \alpha) u_{t-1}$						

References and further reading

Brown, R.G. 1962, *Smoothing, Forecasting and the Prediction of Time Series*. Prentice Hall, New Jersey.

Holt, C.C. 1957, 'Forecasting seasonals by exponentially weighted moving averages', *Office of Naval Research Memo no. 52.*

Lewis, C.D. 1997, *Demand forecasting and inventory control*. Woodhead Publishing, Cambridge.

Wheelwright, S.C., and Makridakis, S. 1985, *Forecasting models for management*, 4th edn. Chichester, UK: Wiley.

Selecting and Monitoring Forecasting Systems for Inventory Control

Because of the adaptability and flexibility of the family of forecasting models based on the exponentially weighted average principle, these tend to predominate in inventory control systems. Hence when choosing which particular forecasting model to use, since more complex models than the simple exponentially weighted average are defined as beyond the scope of this half-book, the choice of model in this case simplifies to the choice of the value of the exponentially smoothing constant α. In the previous chapter it was stated that values of α of either 0.1 or 0.2 represent a compromise between a fixed or static forecast ($\alpha = 0$) or a very sensitive forecast where the one period ahead forecast is equal to the current demand ($\alpha = 1.0$).

Further support to this assertion is given by examining the comparable moving average forecasting system, based on an equally weighted average incorporating n observations, which exponentially weighted averages have now largely replaced. Table 9.1 displays the corresponding values of n (for the moving average) and α (for the exponentially weighted average) which can be shown to produce forecasts with the same *average age of data*. With $n = 12$ (for a weighted moving averages with equal weights of $^1/_n$) being a popular choice (since, for monthly data, it removes seasonal elements based on a yearly cycle) the equivalent value of α (for the exponentially weighted average) is $\alpha = 0.154$. This value, placed more or less midway between 0.1 and 0.2, gives further support for the choice of an α value of either 0.1 or 0.2.

Table 9.1 Table of equivalent values of the α used to form an exponential weighted average and n the corresponding number of periods included within a moving average of the same 'average age of data'

α	n
0.05	39
0.1	19
0.154	12
0.2	9
0.3	6

Statistics for establishing the validity and accuracy of forecasting models

Although typical values of α of 0.1 or 0.2 are often used when forecasting with exponentially weighted average forecasting models, when trying to establish which forecast is *best* in any particular situation, it is necessary to have statistical information available, particularly with regard to the size of the forecasting errors.

The two most used statistics for selecting the suitability of forecasting models are now described in detail.

The mean squared error – MSE

The 'mean squared error' is the average of the squared forecasting errors. As such it is often the statistic used to ascertain the *best* forecasting model, it being assumed that the model with the minimum *MSE* will be *best* where:

$$MSE = \frac{1}{n}\sum_{t=1}^{n} e^2_t \tag{9.1}$$

Referring to Row 5 in Table 8.3 (return to page 152), it can be seen that the mean squared error for this forecasting schedule based on $\alpha = 0.2$ is 147. However, altering the value of α over a practical range from 0.0 to 0.5 produces the results shown in Table 9.2. From these it can be seen that although a value of $\alpha = 0.3$ produces a marginally smaller MSE of 144, any values of above or below either of these two values of α would not produce improved forecasts.

Table 9.2 Mean squared error for different values of α as developed from the forecasting schedule shown originally as Table 2.3

α	0.0	0.1	0.2	0.3	0.4	0.5
MSE	210	160	147	144	152	160

The mean absolute percentage error – MAPE

The 'mean absolute percentage error' is one of the most commonly used statistics in all types of forecasting. It gives an indication of the average size of forecasting error expressed as a percentage of the relevant demand value, irrespective of whether that forecasting error is positive (situation where the forecast under-estimates) or negative (situation where the forecast over-estimates).

In computational terms, if the forecasting error at time t, (that is, e_t) is defined as the demand d_t minus the forecast f_t $(= u_{t-1})$ such that such that $e_t = (d_t - f_t)$, it then follows that the 'mean absolute percentage error' (MAPE) is defined as:

$$MAPE = \frac{100}{n} \sum_{t=1}^{n} \frac{e_t}{d_t} \qquad (9.2)$$

where:

- The | | symbols either side of e_t represent absolute values and, hence, $|e_t|$ is considered positive irrespective of whether e_t is positive or negative, and
- n represents the number of observations involved.

Note: Where zero demand values exist, these must be excluded from the MAPE calculation simply because the result of dividing by zero produces a value of infinity.

Because the MAPE measures the average relative size of the absolute forecasting error as a percentage of the corresponding demand value, in practice a value of less than 10 per cent would be regarded as a very good fit and providing potentially very good forecasts. As a relative measure, its interpretation can be broadly categorized as follows.

MAPE < 10 per cent – forecasts potentially very good
MAPE < 20 per cent – forecasts potentially good
MAPE < 30 per cent – forecasts potentially reasonable
MAPE > 50 per cent – forecasts potentially inaccurate.

Referring to Row 6 in Table 8.3 (return to page 152), it can be seen that for individual months in the forecasting schedule the 'absolute percentage error' varies between 2 and 41 per cent with a resulting Mean Absolute Percentage Error of 12 per cent, a value well within the range for which good forecasts could be expected.

Choice and use of forecasting statistics

Because the MSE is not a relative measure and, therefore, cannot be used to compare the forecasting effectiveness between different data series, its main application is to determine the ideal forecasting parameters (in this case the optimal value of α) for a particular data series as illustrated in Table 9.2.

Because the MAPE is a relative measure, it can be used to compare the forecasting effectiveness between different data series and is particularly useful in determining when a forecasting model is achieving such poor results (with, say, an MAPE>30 per cent) that an alternative approach, such as the prediction of future demand, is necessary.

Monitoring forecast systems

Within any forecasting system it is necessary to monitor the accuracy of the forecasts being produced and to manually correct those forecasts which go out of control due to significant changes in the demand pattern. In this section, the monitoring of short-term forecasts is discussed with particular emphasis placed on those situations where many stocked item forecasts are being produced to establish inventory control parameters.

Most practical forecasting systems which involve many items operate on the basis that if there is no evidence to the contrary then it is assumed that the forecast is in control, that is, there have been no significant changes in the demand pattern to make current forecasts invalid. For such a policy of *management by exception* to operate successfully, clearly an effective monitoring system is essential.

Although several different approaches have been taken with regard to monitoring forecasts, Trigg's (1964) proposal for a tracking signal (known in the US as the 'smoothed error tracking signal') has become an essential part of the majority of comprehensive short-term forecasting systems.

The Trigg or *smoothed error* tracking signal

The tracking signal proposed originally by Trigg is based on the fact that if forecasting errors e_t are defined as demand minus forecast (that is, $e_t = d_t - u_{t-1}$) then the current smoothed error $\overline{e}_t$ is defined as the exponentially weighted average of the forecasting errors e_t and is produced by:

$$\overline{e}_t = \alpha' e_t + (1 - \alpha')\,\overline{e}_{t-1} \tag{9.3}$$

where $\overline{e}_{t-1}$ is the value of the smoothed error for the previous (that is, immediate past) time period.

The current value of mean absolute deviation (MAD) is then defined as the exponentially weighed average of the absolute forecasting errors $|e_t|$ using the formula:

$$MAD_t = \alpha' |e_t| + (1 - \alpha')MAD_{t-1} \tag{9.4}$$

where the absolute value signs $|\ |$ indicate that all errors e_t are treated as positive irrespective of their actual polarity, and where MAD_{t-1} is the value of the mean absolute deviation for the previous time period.

In both Equations 9.3 and 9.4 the parameter α' is an exponential weighting constant (EWC) whose value must be between zero and one. By convention, for monitoring applications α' is set universally at a fixed value of $\alpha' = 0.2$.

Having defined the smoothed error $\overline{e}_t$ and the mean absolute deviation MAD_t, the tracking signal T_t is then defined as the ratio of the smoothed error to the mean absolute deviation, hence:

$$T_t = \overline{e}_t \,/\, MAD_t \tag{9.5}$$

Given that the value of α' used to produce both $\overline{e}_t$ and MAD_t are the same and set at 0.2, then in practice, irrespective of the data involved, the value of the tracking signal can only vary between +1 and –1. This is because in the extreme case where a significant increase in demand has occurred, all forecasting errors are positive and effectively Equations 9.3 and 9.4 become the same and $\overline{e}_t \rightarrow MAD_t$ and hence $T_t \rightarrow +1$. Contrariwise, in the extreme case where a significant decrease in demand has occurred, all forecasting errors are negative and it follows that $\overline{e}_t \rightarrow -MAD_t$ and hence $T_t \rightarrow -1$.

In summary, the value of the tracking signal T_t can be interpreted statistically as follows:

- If the value of the tracking signal exceeds 0.7, the user can be 95 per cent confident in the hypothesis that the accompanying forecast is out of control due to an untypically high set of demand values for which there should be an identifiable, external cause. (Note: *A 95 per cent confidence level means that, on average, only once in twenty occasions would the forecast actually be out of control without the monitoring system detecting the fact. This 95 per cent level of confidence is generally accepted as sufficiently high enough for all practical, forecasting applications.*) A forecast going out of control due to a significant increase in demand could be exemplified, for instance, by the failure of a competitor supplier whose customers have diverted their demand requirements to the inventory holder.

- If the value of the tracking signal is less than –0.7, the user can be 95 per cent confident in the hypothesis that the accompanying forecast is out of control due to an untypically low set of demand values for which there should be an identifiable, external cause. This could, for instance, occur as a result of the inventory holder losing a major customer or a general loss of market share due to financial or legislative changes.

The calculations required to produce a forecasting schedule based on a simple exponentially weighted average with alpha $\alpha = 0.2$ are shown in detail in the rows 7, 8 and 9 of Table 8.3. In detail, the calculations involved (assuming $\alpha' = 0.2$) are as follows:

- Row 7: for the month of January, although the smoothed error is calculated as $\overline{e}_t = \alpha' e_t + (1 - \alpha')\,\overline{e}_{t-1}$, with the assumption that an unbiased estimate of the previous smoothed error $\overline{e}_{t-1} = 0$, then $\overline{e}_t = 0.2 \times |5| = 1$. For the next month, February $\overline{e}_t = 0.2 \times -1 + (1 - 0.2) \times 1 = 0.6$.
- Row 8: for the month of January, when calculating the Mean Absolute Deviation using $MAD_t = \alpha' |e_t| + (1 - \alpha')MAD_{t-1}$, it is necessary to make an assumption for the previous value of the Mean Absolute Deviation MAD_{t-1}. If this is not done the value of the tracking signal starts at 1, indicating the forecast is totally out of control, hardly a useful start! A sensible rule to cover this situation is to assume, when starting up only, that: $MAD_{t-1} = 0.1 \times u_{t-1}$. Hence, the initial value of MAD_t is given by $MAD_t = 0.2 \times |5| + (1 - 0.2) \times 0.1 \times 50 = 5.0$.
  For the next month, February
  $MAD_t = 0.2 \times |-1| + (1 - 0.2) \times 5.0 = 4.2$.
- Row 9: the tracking signal is simply evaluated as the ratio of the smoothed error $\overline{e}_t$ to the Mean Absolute Deviation MAD_t. Hence for January $T_t = 1.0/5.0 = 0.2$ and for February $T_t = 0.6/4.2 = 0.1$ indicating that the assumptions made above do indeed ensure that the tracking signal is started with some sensible values.

It is interesting to note that the value of the tracking signal equals 0.7 in May, successfully identifying (at a 95 per cent confidence level) the significantly high demand impulse of 86 which occurs in that month. It should be also noted that the less obvious increase in demand values over the months October to December, produces a cumulative effect which is identified as a significant increase in demand with a tracking signal of 0.7 being registered in December.

Implementing a monitoring system based on the Trigg or *smoothed error* tracking signal

In an inventory situation, to operate monitoring system based on the principle of *management by exception*, a comprehensive method of implementing the Trigg or *smoothed error* tracking signal would be to:

- Calculate the value of the tracking signal for all items;
- Exclude from consideration those items for which the tracking signal had already indicated an out of control situation;
- Of those items that remain, list those items for which the absolute value of the tracking signal exceeds a value of 0.7 (that is, include all items for which one is 95 per cent confident that there has either been a significant *rise* or *fall* in demand) in descending order of the absolute value of the tracking signal, and
- Investigate the top N items in the resulting list as items for which the forecasting system is now indicating it can no longer produce sensible forecasts, where N is the number of items for which there are sufficient resources to investigate the reasons for the out of control situation being created and for which manual corrections need to be made.

In addition it is necessary to check that:

- The forecast is producing reasonable results and is typically achieving a mean absolute error of less than 20 per cent, and
- The forecast is in control and is typically achieving a an absolute tracking signal value of less than 0.7.

Conclusion

With all forecasting systems it is necessary to maintain a check on the overall performance of the product forecasts and to identify specific, unusual demands which might invalidate even an effective forecasting system for a period of time subsequent to the occurrence of that unusual demand. To check that the forecast is in control, the Trigg or *smoothed error* tracking signal should be calculated whose absolute value should consistently be below 0.7.

With regard to the overall effectiveness of the forecasting system, it is necessary to check that the individual forecasts are typically achieving a mean absolute percentage error of less than 20 per cent.

Question

1. Complete rows 5 to 9 of the forecasting schedule shown below.

		Jan	Feb	Mar	Apr	May	Jun
1	**Current period's demand** d_t	123	100	178	122	86	52
2	**Current period's forecast** $f_t = u_{t-1}$	100*					
3	**Current period's forecast error** $e_t = d_t - f_t$						
4	**One period ahead forecast** $f_{t+1} = u_t = \alpha d_t + (1 - \alpha) u_{t-1}$						
5	**Squared Error** e_t^2						
6	**Absolute Percentage Error** $\text{APE} = 100\, \lvert e_t \rvert / d_t$						
7	**Smoothed error** $\bar{e}_t = 0.2e_t + (1 - 0.2)\, \bar{e}_{t-1}$						
8	**Mean Absolute Deviation** $\text{MAD}_t = 0.2\lvert e_t \rvert + (1 - 0.2)\, \text{MAD}_{t-1}$						
9	**Tracking signal** $T_t = \bar{e}_t / \text{MAD}_t$						

References and further reading

Batty, M. 1969, 'Monitoring an exponential smoothing forecasting system', *Operational Research Quarterly*, 20, p. 391.

Brown, R.G. 1962, *Smoothing, forecasting and predictions of discrete time series*. Prentice Hall, New Jersey.

Barron, M. and Targett, D. 1985, *The Manager's Guide to Business Forecasting*. Blackwell, Oxford.

Lewis, C.D. 1982, *Industrial and Business Forecasting Methods*. Butterworths, London.

Gilchrist, W. 1982, *Statistical Forecasting*. Wiley, Chichester.

Trigg, D.W. 1964, 'Monitoring a forecasting system', *Operational Research Quarterly*, 15, p. 271.

10 The Re-order Level Inventory Policy: Setting the Re-order Level

THE two principal rules controlling a re-order level policy are:

1. When the stock-on-hand falls to or below a pre-specified level, an order for replenishment is raised immediately, and
2. The size of that replenishment order is a relatively fixed value.

In this chapter, the calculation of the size of the re-order level will be discussed and Chapter 11 will concentrate on establishing the size of the replenishment quantity.

The re-order level (ROL) policy

The most commonly used inventory control policy is the re-order level policy, within which a relatively fixed size replenishment order is placed when the stock-on-hand (that is, physical stock held plus outstanding replenishments less committed stock) falls to or below a level known as the re-order level.

This replenishment order is normally delayed by a period known as the 'lead-time', this being the delay between the order actually being placed and the goods being not only received by the organization placing the order but also processed by that organization, such that the goods are actually available for issue to customers. Situations where stocks run out (that is, fall to zero) and none is available to satisfy customers, are referred to as stockouts.

For the re-order level policy, the duration of the lead-time is the policy's so called *period of risk*, this being the time during which stocks are at risk of running out. This occurs since once the re-order level has been equalled or broken and the order for replenishment placed, within the rules of the policy no remedial action can be taken to prevent a stockout occurring. Clearly a stockout will occur if the demand during the lead-time turns out to be significantly higher than usual, and more specifically, higher than the value of the re-order level.

Figure 10.1 shows simulated stock balances for a re-order level policy over a three year period and indicates when orders for replenishment are raised (ord) – as a result of the re-order level being equalled or *broken* – and subsequently received (rec) after the lead-time delay, which in this particular situation is set at four months.

For the three year period shown here, a re-order level value of 260 units appears to achieve a reasonable balance, as no stockouts occur during the three years being considered and unused stock (the gap between minimum stocks and zero stock) is never excessively high.

Examination of Figure 10.1 confirms that the operation of the re-order level inventory control policy is determined completely by the setting of just two parameters, namely the value of the *re-order level* and the value of the *replenishment quantity*.

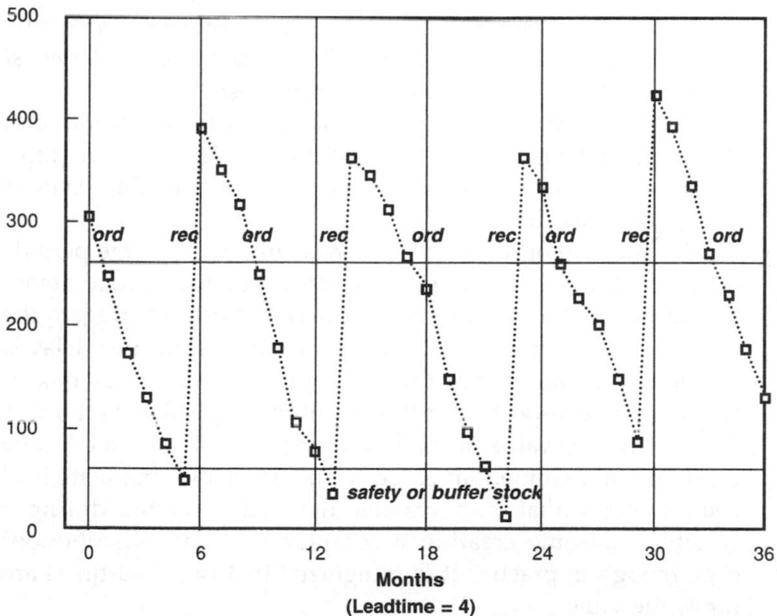

Figure 10.1 Re-order level policy stock balances for a three year period

The traditional approach to establishing the value of the re-order level

To establish an appropriate value for the re-order level it is necessary to estimate or assume values for:

- $\bar{D}$ – the average demand per unit of time (usually estimated from a short-term forecast – see page 149). The higher the average demand, the more stock required to meet the average demand during the lead-time.
- σ_d – the standard deviation of demand per unit of time (usually estimated from the Mean Absolute Deviation established from the short-term forecast as, $\sigma_d = 1.25MAD_t$ – see page 159).

  (Note: *For the normal distribution the constant defining the relationship between the standard deviation and Mean Absolute Deviation is theoretically equal to* $\sqrt{\pi/2} = 1.2587$ *and it has become standard practice to use a value of 1.25. This method of evaluating the standard deviation of demand per unit time,* σ_d, *has proved quite accurate enough for most inventory control situations and much simpler than the conventional root mean square calculation which would require past data and forecasting values to be stored. This clearly would also not be appropriate for all the reasons levelled against moving average forecasting models –* *see page 148*).

  A higher variability of demand (and hence a larger value of the standard deviation of demand during the lead-time) requires more stock to absorb those variations if a reasonable level of service is to be achieved.
- L – the duration of the lead-time, measured in the same periods or units of time as that on which the average and standard deviation of demand are based. Since the re-order level triggers the placing of a replenishment order, the resulting lead-time delay is the period of time when the stock control policy is at risk of running out, irrespective of the size of that replenishment order. The duration or value of the lead-time is usually assumed to be fixed at an assumed average value to avoid mathematical complications (that is, a variable demand occurring during a variable lead-time creating a complex bi-variate distribution) even though in practice it is recognized that two lead-times are rarely the same.

In addition to the above, it is necessary to make an assumption as to the likely probability distribution of demand during the lead-time. With regard to this latter point, for reasonably fast moving items with an average demand of twenty units or more per time period, it is usual to assume that the demand during the lead-time is likely to be normally distributed. Where this is not the case, treatment for other distributions can be found in Waters (1992).

Table 10.1 shows, in numerical form, the stock balances for the first twelve months for the situation shown previously in Figure 10.1. Examining the detail of this table shows that the stock balances have resulted from a situation where:

- The demand per unit time was specified to be distributed normally with an average $\bar{D}L = 50$ units/month and a standard deviation $\sigma_d = 15$ units/month, whereas the average values actually generated by the simulation model for this particular sequence were only marginally different at 49.46 and 15.66 respectively, and
- The duration of the lead-time delay in obtaining replenishments was fixed at L = 4 months.

It was then assumed that the demand during the lead-time would also be distributed normally with:

- an average of $\bar{D}L = 50 \times 4 = 200$ units/lead-time, and
- a standard deviation of $\sigma_d\sqrt{L} = 15\sqrt{4} = 30$ units/lead-time.

(Note: In statistical terms, since the variance of a sample varies with the size of the sample, the standard deviation – which is the square-root of the variance – varies with the square-root of the sample size. In this case, because the demand during the lead-time is being estimated, the lead-time duration is effectively the sample size and $\sigma_d\sqrt{L}$ (that is, $15\sqrt{4} = 30$) is therefore the best estimated value of the standard deviation of demand during the lead-time.)

If the re-order level were to be set at a value equal to the average demand during the lead-time $\bar{D}L$ (that is, $50 \times 4 = 200$, an amount referred to as *turnover stock* since this would be the amount of stock expected be turned over if demand during the lead-time were to be equal to the average), since the probability of exceeding the average for a normal distribution (and indeed all symmetrical distributions) is 50 per cent, the probability of a subsequent stockout occurring would be also be 50 per cent. This can be seen in Figure 10.2 which is a plot of a normal distribution with a mean of 200 units and a standard deviation of 30.

Table 10.1 Table of simulated stock balances for a re-order level policy subject to a demand situation where average demand ($\bar{D}$) = 50 and standard deviation of demand (σ_d) = 15 with a lead-time of 4. The actual re-order level controlling the simulation is set equal to the theoretical value of 260 computed using Equation 10.1.

COSTS:		
Storage (% pa mat'l cost)	22.50%	
Material (+ lab + o'heads)	1.00	
Ordering cost/occasion	30.00	
Penalty cost/period	30.00	

DEMAND/ MONTH	***Specified***	***Actual***
Fcst average	50.00	49.46
Fcst std dev	15.00	15.66
Leadtime (1 to 8)	4	
STOCKTURN		**2.79**

PARAMETERS:	***Specified***	***Theoretical***
Re-order level	260	260
Replenishment quantity	400	400
Vendor service level	87.5%	97.7%
Customer service level	99.2%	99.5%

SIMULATED COSTS/ANNUM	
Storage costs	48.28
Ordering costs	45.00
Penalty costs	12.50
Total operating costs	**105.78**

Months	**Previous stock**	**Current demand**	**Received orders**	**Stock-on-hand**	**Overshoot amount**	**Size of replenishment order placed (fixed)**
0	364	54		310		
1	310	60		250	10	400
2	250	65		185	*= (260 – 250)*	
3	185	72		113		
4	113	59		54		
5	54	33		21		
6	21	49	400	372		
7	372	40		332		
8	332	32		300		
9	300	55		245	15	400
10	245	60		185	*= (260 – 245)*	
11	185	85		100		

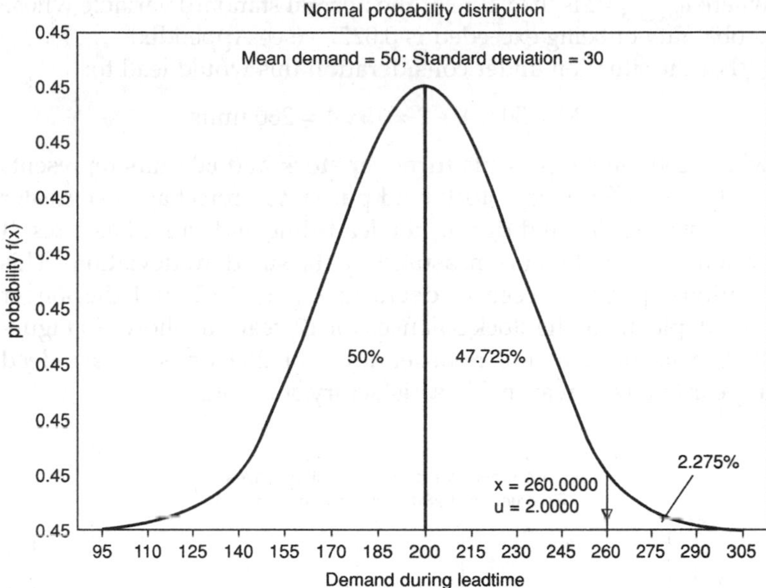

Figure 10.2 Normal distribution indicating with average set at $\bar{D}$L = 200 and the standard deviation set at $\sigma_d\sqrt{L}$ = 30 that the probability of exceeding 260 is 0.02275 or 2.275 per cent. Hence probability of *not* running out is equal to 97.725 per cent.

Clearly a 50 per cent probability of running out of stock subsequent to placing a replenishment order is unlikely to offer an acceptable level of service to any inventory control system's customers. In practice, therefore, to offer a satisfactory level of service, the re-order level would need to be set at a value greater than the average demand during the lead-time by the addition of a further amount of stock known as the safety (or buffer) stock.

To establish a maximum expected demand during the lead-time (rather than the average) an additional degree of protection, say 47.735 per cent, is chosen. This produces an overall 97.725 per cent protection (that is, 50 + 47.735) which can then be interpreted such that the probability of that maximum expected demand value not being exceeded is 2.275 per cent. The re-order level M could be set equal to the maximum expected demand during the lead-time using Equation 4.1:

$$\mathrm{M} = \bar{D}\mathrm{L} + u_{0.02275}\sigma_d\sqrt{\mathrm{L}} \qquad (10.1)$$

where $u_{0.02275}= 2$ is the value of the normal standard variable whose probability of being exceeded is 0.02275 (see Appendix).

For the situation under consideration this would lead to:

$$M = 50 \times 4 + 2 \times 15\sqrt{4} = 260 \text{ units}$$

where 200 units represents turnover stock and 60 units represents safety (or buffer) stock: stock held purely to protect against greater than average demand during the lead-time and caused as a result of demand variation (as measured by the standard deviation). This relationship can be seen in detail in Figure 10.2, and the longer overall picture of the stock balances for 12 years, as shown in Figure 10.3, confirms that the re-order level of 260 units does indeed appear to offer a reasonably satisfactory solution.

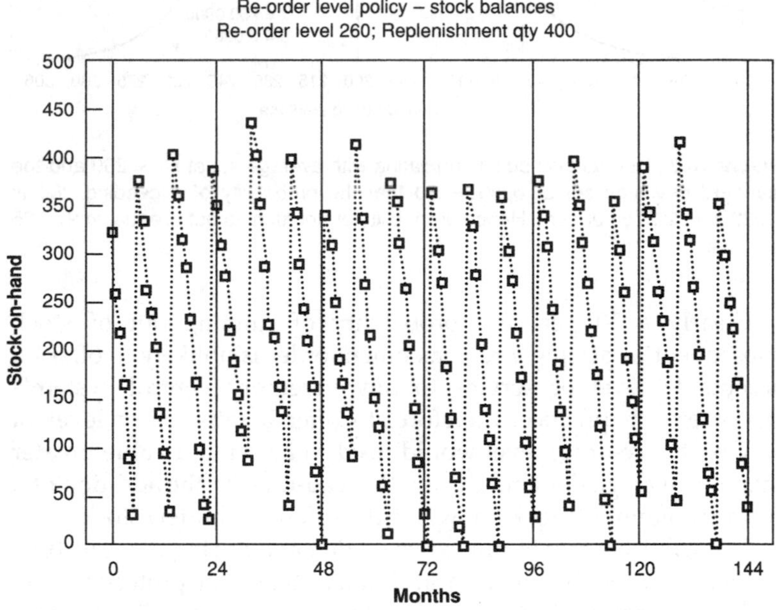

Figure 10.3 Re-order level policy stock balances for a 12 year period

The relatively simple statistical relationship just described has been used to establish that if an order for replenishment were to be raised when the stock-on-hand was *exactly* equal to the re-order level, then in theory on 97.752 per cent of these occasions when the inventory control system was at risk of a stockout subsequent to a replenishment order being placed, demand during the lead-time would be less than the value of the re-order level and no stockout would occur. Conversely, on 2.275 per cent of those occasions, demand during the lead-time would exceed the value of the re-order level and a stockout would occur.

Therefore, on the assumption that demand during the lead-time could be assumed to be normally distributed, this procedure establishes the value of the re-order level by defining a 'vendor service level' as being the *probability of not running out of stock on those occasions when the policy was at risk of running out*, that is, the probability of a stockout *not* occurring subsequent to an order for replenishment being raised but prior to its being received. This traditional approach of setting the re-order level value within a re-order level inventory policy by defining a 'vendor service level' can be criticized on several counts, and will be in Chapter 12. However it still remains a popular method since, in spite of its flaws, the approach still in practice achieves very acceptable results.

The two-bin system

In practice, the re-order level inventory policy can be implemented as what is generally referred to as a *two-bin system*. In this situation demand is normally met by withdrawals from a first bin (see Figure 10.4). When this first bin is emptied by a demand withdrawal, a replenishment order is placed. Further demand, during the lead-time delay between the placing of this replenishment order and its receipt, is then met by withdrawals from a second bin. The size of this second bin then effectively becomes the re-order level. A simplification of this procedure is to combine both bins into a single, with a mark in this single bin indicating the re-order level.

For such a system to operate effectively, the volume occupied by the stocked part must be representative of the number of stocked units held. Clearly, this is only likely to be true for relatively small parts such as (in a manufacturing situation) nuts, bolts and washers. Thus, in practice, such small parts are often indeed held within a *two- or one-bin system* where formal stock recording is not maintained and replenishments are simply ordered when the first of the two bins becomes empty. This saves considerably on administrative costs, as will be discussed in Chapter 12. Any small increase in storage costs caused as a result of not keeping accurate control via formal forecasting and so on, should be more than offset by these administrative savings.

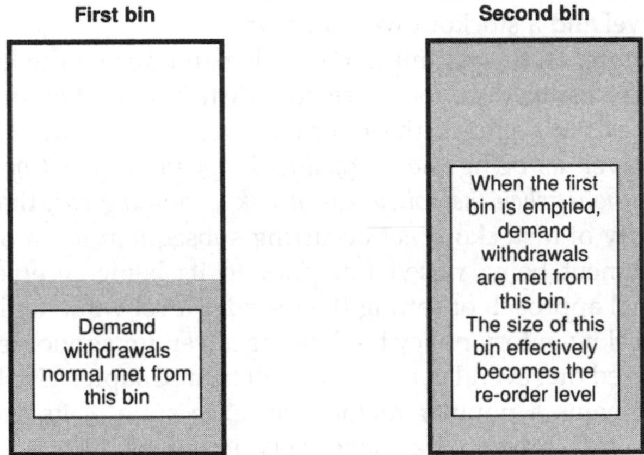
First bin
Second bin
Demand withdrawals normal met from this bin
When the first bin is emptied, demand withdrawals are met from this bin. The size of this bin effectively becomes the re-order level

Figure 10.4 Representation of a two-bin stock control system in operation (assumes volume representative of quantity)

Conclusion

The setting of a re-order level to trigger the placing of replenishment orders is one of the most popular methods of raising orders to replenish an inventory system. The approach has an intuitive appeal and, when the item being stocked is physically small or a powder or liquid, and hence it can be assumed that the volume occupied is proportional to the quantity held, a re-order level policy can then be implemented as a so-called *two-bin* system within which, when a first bin is emptied, a replenishment order is placed and material is then withdrawn from a second bin whose capacity is equivalent to the re-order level.

The main advantage of the re-order level policy is that it tends to keep stocks relatively low leading to low stockholding costs, but against this must be set the policy's main disadvantage; namely that the policy is one of continuous review in which replenishment orders can be triggered at any point in time, leading to relatively high replenishment costs due to this irregularity: see Waters (1992).

The analysis of the re-order level calculations covered in this chapter to establish the value of the re-order level cover the standard treatment based on the assumption of a normal distribution of demand and fixed lead-time. Treatments for other demand distributions and situations involving variable lead-times are covered in texts noted under 'Further reading' at the end of this chapter.

Questions

1. For a demand situation where the average demand per week was 300 units and the standard deviation 40, and replenishment orders were delayed on average by two weeks, within a re-order level policy what re-order level would be required to offer a *vendor service level* or probability of not running out of stock per occasion of 96 per cent?
2. For the situation described in question 1, what *vendor service level* or probability of not running out of stock per occasion would be offered by a re-order level of 720 units?

References and further reading

Buffa, E.S. and Miller, J.G. 1987, *Modern Production Operations*. Wiley, Chichester, New York, Toronto.

Bolton, W. 1994, *Production Planning and Control*. Longman, London.

Harrison, M. *Finite Capacity Scheduling – The Art of Synchronized Manufacturing*. Woodhead Publishing, Cambridge.

Hill, T. 1983, *Production and Operations Management*, Prentice Hall, New Jersey.

Karush, W. 1957, 'A Queuing Model for an Inventory Problem', Operational Research Quarterly, 5.

Lockyer, K. Muhlemann, A. and Oakland, J. 1988, *Production and Operations Management*. Pitman, London.

Thomas, A.B. 1980, *Stock Control in Manufacturing Industries*. Gower Press, London.

Urry, S. 1991, *Introduction to Operational Research*. Longman, Harlow.

Waters, C.D.J. 1992, *Inventory Control and Management*. Wiley, Chichester, New York, Toronto.

Wild, R. 1980, *Essentials of Operations Management*. Holt, Rinehart & Winston, New York.

The Re-order Level Inventory Policy: Establishing the Size of the Replenishment Quantity

Introduction

In Chapter 10 the setting of the value of the re-order level within a re-order level inventory control policy was established solely on the basis of offering a statistically defined level of service. Having established the value of the re-order level, traditionally the size of the replenishment order has then been determined using a totally unrelated approach of minimizing the annual costs of operating that inventory policy (that is, the costs of ordering and storage). This approach produces a value for the replenishment quantity which is often referred to as the Economic Order Quantity (EOQ).

As with the method of establishing the value of the re-order level, this EOQ method of establishing the value of the replenishment quantity also has many critics. However, the approach is both well known and widely used and has yet to be supplanted by an alternative approach that has as wide an appeal. However, to place the EOQ in perspective, some of the criticisms of the approach will be addressed in this chapter. The particular criticism that the replenishment quantity should not be evaluated separately on a cost basis, but should be considered jointly with the evaluation of the re-order level, is considered in Chapter 12.

The Economic Order Quantity (EOQ) approach to establishing the value of the replenishment quantity.

The theory behind establishing the value of the replenishment quantity dates back to the closing years of the nineteenth century but the drawing of attention to the approach, particularly to the business world, has been generally attributed to Wilson who, as early as 1934 proposed evaluating the size q of the replenishment order on a basis of minimizing the annual costs of *operating* an inventory policy, these costs being assumed to be a combination of the annual costs of ordering replenishment orders and the costs of storing inventory.

The underlying assumptions of this approach to determine the size of the replenishment quantity q are that:

- Ordering costs (that is, costs of raising replenishment orders) per annum are assumed to be equal to the number of replenishment orders multiplied by the cost C_o of raising each individual order; where C_o is assumed to be independent of the order size. Establishing from a forecasting analysis that the annual demand is estimated as A, then the annual cost of raising $\frac{A}{q}$ replenishment orders per annum is given as:

  $$\left(\frac{A}{q}\right)C_o$$

  where, for monthly demand estimated at $\bar{D}$, the annual demand $A = 12\bar{D}$, but for weekly demand $A = 50\bar{D}$, for a 50 week working year.

- Storage costs per annum are assumed to be based on the average level of stock held, this latter being evaluated as half the replenishment order size q (that is, $\frac{q}{2}$) plus a fixed amount of safety stock s.
  (Note: The safety stock s is that stock held purely to protect against greater than average demand during the lead-time and evaluated as $u_{0.02275}\sigma_d\sqrt{L}$ in Equation 10.1, see page 169).

Given that a stocked item's value (unit material cost) is C_m and that the holding cost stock per annum is given as i per cent of the item's value C_m, it then follows that the costs of storage per annum are equal to the average stock $(\frac{q}{2} + s)$ multiplied by the unit cost of storage per annum iC_m. Annual storage costs are, therefore, evaluated as:

$$\left(\frac{q}{2} + s\right) iC_m$$

It then follows that if the annual costs C_A of operating an inventory policy can be assumed to be equal to the costs of ordering replenishments plus the costs of storage, then:

$$C_A = \left(\frac{A}{q}\right) C_o + \left(\frac{q}{2} + s\right) iC_m. \qquad (11.1)$$

By differentiating the annual operating costs C_A (as defined by Equation 11.1) with respect to the replenishment order quantity q and assuming the safety stock s is either fixed, or at least independent of q, we obtain:

$$\frac{dC_A}{dq} = \frac{AC_o}{q^2} + \frac{iC_m}{2}. \qquad (11.2)$$

On the basis that ordering costs decrease but that storage costs increase with replenishment order size, it can be shown that there must be a replenishment order size which minimizes annual operating costs. These minimum operating costs occur at a replenishment order size corresponding to that position where the tangent to the total operating cost curve is zero, that is, $\frac{dC_A}{dq} = 0$.

This results in a value for the replenishment quantity, referred to as the Economic Order Quantity, Q_o, which is calculated by the well known square-root formula developed as the solution to Equation 11.2 when $\frac{dC_A}{dq} = 0$, and produces:

$$Q_o = \sqrt{\frac{2AC_o}{iC_m}}. \qquad (11.3)$$

Readers unfamiliar with calculus can rest assured that these results are valid since the Economic Order Quantity is one of the most publicly debated topics in management science.

To illustrate the use of the EOQ equation, the initial stock control situation depicted earlier in Chapter 10 is further defined by the following input information:

- A (annual demand) = $12 \times \bar{D} = 600$ with $\bar{D} = 50$ units per month
- C_o (the cost of raising an order per occasion) = 30
- i (the annual holding interest rate) = 22.5 per cent (that is, 0.225); and
- C_m (the stocked item's unit value) = 1.00.

By substituting in Equation 11.3, the Economic Order Quantity Q_o is evaluated as:

$$Q_o = \sqrt{\frac{2 \times 600 \times 30}{0.225 \times 1}} = 400 \text{ units.}$$

The calculations above can be confirmed by examining Figure 11.1 which illustrates that:

- Costs of ordering can be seen to fall rapidly as the size of replenishment order increases since fewer, larger orders are needed to meet the same annual demand;
- Costs of storage can be seen to rise linearly with replenishment order size since the average stock held also rises with increased replenishment order size, and
- The annual operating costs, equal to the sum of the ordering and storage costs, can be seen to be a minimum at the point at which the costs of ordering and storage intersect and where in addition the differential to the operating cost curve $\frac{dC_A}{dq} = 0$.

In considering the above treatment of the Economic Order Quantity calculation, readers are again reminded that inventory control should not be treated as an exact science. The EOQ should be regarded, therefore, as an indication of an appropriate replenishment order size which should produce reasonable stock balances. Indeed in practice it will often be necessary to round up any replenishment order size to the quantity of items contained in the appropriate carton, container, pallet, and so on, as the additional cost of splitting any of these packaging units would be prohibitive. The reason for recommending *rounding up* rather than *rounding down* is that storage costs increase less rapidly with larger order sizes than ordering costs increase with smaller order sizes, as can be seen clearly in Figure 11.1, overleaf.

Criticisms of the Economic Order Quantity approach

There are many criticisms of the simple Economic Order Quantity approach, some of which are that:

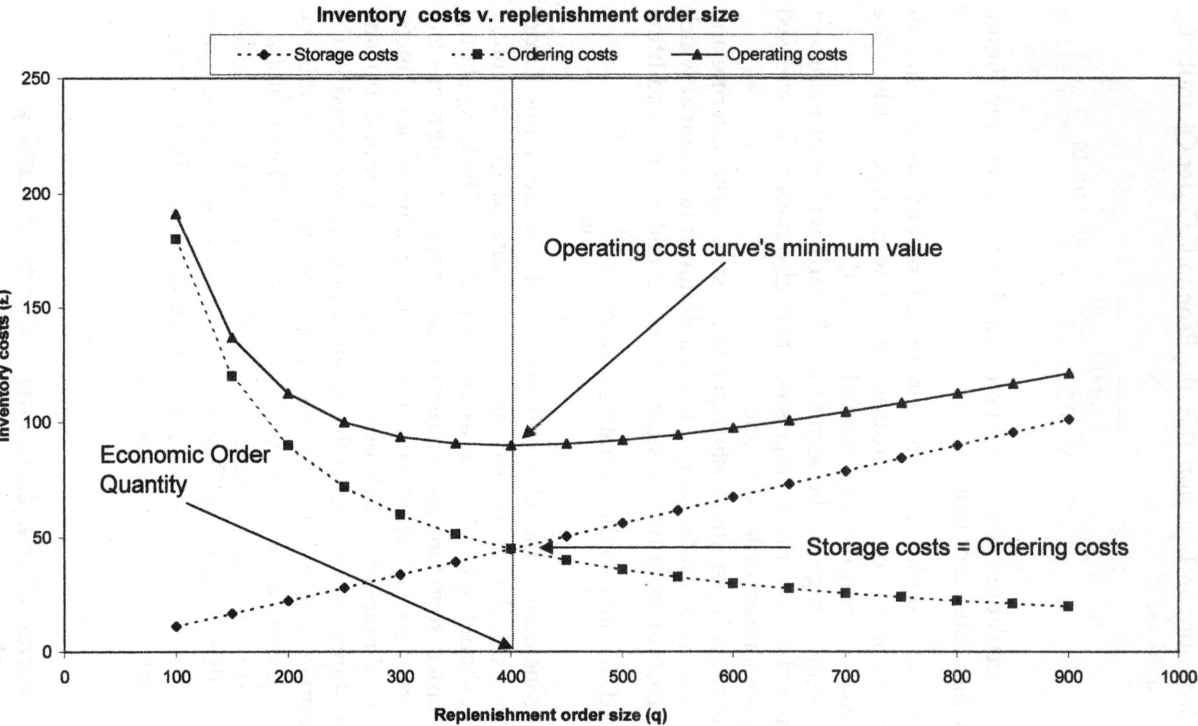

Figure 11.1 Costs of operating, storing and ordering for an inventory system compared with replenishment order size

- The costs involved in the formulation of the EOQ are difficult to estimate with any great accuracy, and that the storage cost in particular may not increase linearly with replenishment order size but incrementally as storage capacity limits are reached.
- Rather than minimizing costs the EOQ should be formulated on an alternative criterion such as that of maximizing profit, or return on investment.
- Because the total operating cost curve is so shallow it makes little difference whether the chosen replenishment quantity is near to the EOQ or not.
- The EOQ approach does not take into account the possibility of achieving price breaks by placing large replenishment orders on suppliers.

These criticisms will now be examined in detail.

Difficulties in estimating costs

It has already been pointed out that the EOQ should not be regarded as a precise replenishment order size whose value, as evaluated using Equation 11.3, is to be treated as sacrosanct. Inaccuracies in estimating costs are a fact of everyday life and in practice often tend to balance out each other or, in the particular case of the EOQ calculations, have their effect significantly reduced by the action of the square-root function in Equation 11.3 – see Eilon (1962) for extensive treatment of this effect.

Alternative criteria for establishing an optimal replenishment order size

Many authors have considered alternative criteria to establish the replenishment order size rather than minimizing costs; but however much the EOQ is criticized it does in practice produce reasonable results based on a relatively simple equation (see discussion on page 184).

Cost sensitivity of the EOQ approach in establishing the replenishment order size

As has already been noted; it can be seen from Figure 11.1 that if a replenishment quantity other than the EOQ were to be used, since storage costs increase linearly above the EOQ whereas ordering costs increase more steeply below the EOQ, then proportionately it would be preferable to place a replenishment order larger than the EOQ rather than smaller. This general observation can be confirmed algebraically by considering the general case of replenishment order q whose size is x per cent larger or smaller then the EOQ, Q_o.

Given that:

$$q = Q_o\left(1 \pm \frac{x}{100}\right)$$

it follows that if safety stock s can be ignored since it is independent of replenishment order size, then the annual operating costs of C_q of operating at q rather than at Q_o will be given by transposing Equation 11.1 such that:

$$C_q = \frac{AC_o}{Q_o\left(1 \pm \frac{x}{100}\right)} + Q_o\left(1 \pm \frac{x}{100}\right)\frac{iC_m}{2} \qquad (11.4)$$

and that the cost C_{Q_o} of operating at Q_o will be given as:

$$C_{Q_o} = \frac{AC_o}{Q_o} + \frac{Q_o iC_m}{2}\,. \qquad (11.5)$$

Simplifying and combining the relationships expressed in Equations 11.4 and 11.5, it can be shown that the percentage increase in annual operating costs y per cent resulting from using a replenishment order size x per cent higher or lower than the EOQ is given by:

$$y = \left(\frac{C_q}{C_{Q_o}} - 1\right) = \frac{x^2}{2(1+x)} \qquad (11.6)$$

Thus in the situation under consideration, if a replenishment order size of 1000 were to be used, the percentage increase in size relative to the EOQ of 400 would be given by:

$$x = \left(\frac{q}{Q_o} - 1\right) = \left(\frac{1000}{400} - 1\right) = 1.5 \text{ or } 150 \text{ per cent}$$

hence the percentage increase in annual operating costs would be:

$$y = \frac{x^2}{2(1+x)} = \frac{1.5 \times 1.5}{2 \times (1 + 1.5)} = 0.45 \text{ or } 45 \text{ per cent.}$$

By defining a range of replenishment order sizes x per cent higher or lower than the EOQ, the relationship expressed in Equation 11.6 can be seen in detail in Table 11.1.

Table 11.1 Detailing the percentage increase in annual operating costs when specifying a replenishment quantity q chosen to be larger or smaller than the EOQ, Q_o.

Percentage increase or decrease in replenishment quantity q as compared with the EOQ, Q_o	x%	−50	−25	0	+25	+50	+75	+100
Percentage increase in annual *operating* costs	y%	25.00	4.17	0	2.50	8.33	16.07	25.00

Examination of Table 11.1 confirms the fact that replenishment quantities larger than the EOQ involve proportionately lower increases in the annual operating cost than smaller quantities. Hence in the situation being considered here, a replenishment order size 50 per cent larger than the EOQ causes an 8.33 per cent increase in annual operating costs whereas an order size 50 per cent smaller causes a much larger increase of 25 per cent. Table 11.1 also demonstrates that the rate of increase in annual operating costs in both situations is significantly smaller than the imposed proportionate increase or decrease in the size of the replenishment order.

Discount required on purchase price (unit material cost) to reduce the annual total costs of running an inventory policy

Although the previous discussion has indicated that in theory inventory operating costs will increase if replenishment order sizes larger or smaller than the EOQ are used, from a practical point of view such increases must be put into perspective.

Figure 11.2 shows the relative size of the annual costs of ordering and storage compared with the actual annual purchasing/acquisition costs of the item under consideration (that is, the actual costs of purchasing or acquiring the equivalent of a year's annual customer demand). As can be seen very clearly in Figure 11.2, the annual purchase/acquisition costs are an order of magnitude higher than the combined cost of ordering replenishments and storing the item under consideration. In the previous section of this chapter it was shown that when operating with a replenishment order size larger or smaller than the EOQ, a relatively small increase in annual operating cost occurred. However, if the choice of a replenishment order size larger than the EOQ were to be matched by a discount in unit purchase price, because the annual purchasing/acquisition costs – which are directly influenced by any potential price discount – are so much larger than the combined ordering and storage costs, even a very small percentage price discount for larger replenishment order sizes can offset the proportionately small increase in these costs that will be incurred by operating with the larger quantity.

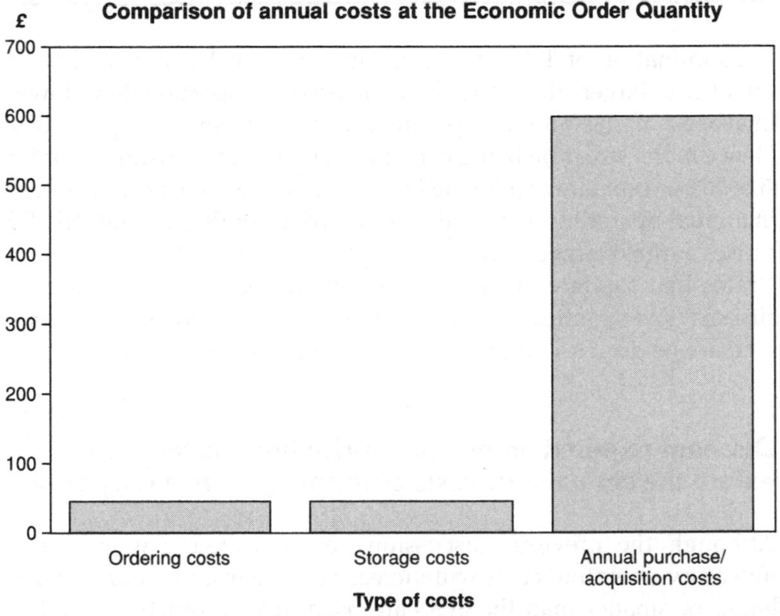

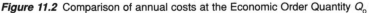

Figure 11.2 Comparison of annual costs at the Economic Order Quantity Q_0

In practice there are many situations where, by ordering a larger replenishment order than the recommended EOQ, it is possible to negotiate a discount on unit price. Such opportunities occur, for instance, when a package or container size is involved and a discount is offered in preference to splitting the package or container.

Given that the proposed replenishment quantity at which a discount is on offer is x per cent larger than the EOQ, it can be shown (see Lewis 1998) that the percentage discount δ_T required to achieve equal total annual inventory costs (that is, annual ordering + storage costs + purchase/acquisition) C_T can be defined by:

$$\delta_T > \frac{C_o x^2}{(1 + x)(C_o(1 + x) + Q_o C_m)} \tag{11.7}$$

which for the order size of 1000 units, 150 per cent larger than the EOQ, and for values of C_o, Q_o and C_m quoted earlier, would require that the discount on purchase price be greater than:

$$d_T > \frac{30 \times 1.52}{(1 + 1.5) \times (30 \times (1 + 1.5) + 400 \times 1)} = 0.005684 \text{ or } 5.684\%,$$

putting the minimum bid price per unit at 0.9432.

To check this solution, the annual operating costs (ordering and storage costs) are as defined by Equation 11.1 and the annual purchase/acquisition costs are AC_m giving a total annual inventory cost of C_T (assuming $s = 0$) defined by:

$$C_T = \left(\frac{A}{q}\right)C_o + \left(\frac{q}{2}\right)iC_m + AC_m \tag{11.8}$$

At the Economic Order Quantity where $q = Q_o = 400$ units and the purchase price per unit is $C_m = 1.00$, it follows that the total annual inventory cost is given by:

$$C_T = \left(\frac{600}{400}\right) \times 30 + \left(\frac{400}{2}\right) \times 0.225 \times 1 + 600 \times 1$$

$$C_T = 45 + 45 + 600 = 900.$$

At the increased order quantity $q = 1000$ units and the discounted purchase price $C_m = 0.9432$ it follows that the total annual inventory cost is given by:

$$C_T = \left(\frac{600}{1000}\right) \times 30 + \left(\frac{1000}{2}\right) \times 0.225 \times 0.9432 + 600 \times 0.9432$$

$$C_T = 18 + 106.1 + 565.9 = 690.$$

Thus verifying that even at the price discount of only 5.684 per cent, the effect of this small discount on the proportionately larger purchase/acquisition costs allows for the total annual inventory costs to remain the same even for a replenishment order size two-and-half times larger than the EOQ.

For a range of increased replenishment orders sizes greater than the EOQ, Table 11.2 demonstrates the discounts which would be required to equal total annual operating costs.

Table 5.2 Percentage discount on unit price required to maintain total annual inventory cost at or below that incurred at the EOQ

Percentage Increase in replenishment quantity q as compared with the EOQ	x%	25	50	75	100	150	200
Price discount required to match total annual inventory cost when $C_m = 1.00$, $C_o = 30$, $i = 22.5$ per cent, $A = 600$ and $Q_o = 400$	δ_T%	0.34	1.12	2.13	3.26	5.68	8.16

Conclusion

The formulation of a replenishment order size known as the 'Economic Order Quantity' is the most discussed single topic in management science generally and also perhaps the most criticized. This chapter, in describing the EOQ concept, has examined some of these criticisms. Other authors have confirmed that while the particular value of an EOQ might well be open to criticism, the overall concept does have considerable merit. In particular the approach known as *Coverage Analysis* – originally proposed by Murdoch (1981) whose underlying principle has achieved a high level of acceptance – proposes that the number of replenishment orders placed per annum, *n*, should be made proportional to the square-root of the annual usage value AC_m as follows:

$$n = k\sqrt{AC_m}$$

where *k* is a constant.

Given that with an annual demand *A* being replenished by *n* orders of size *q* per year, this approach leads to a replenishment order size defined by:

$$q = \frac{A}{n} = \frac{A}{k\sqrt{AC_m}} = \frac{1}{k}\sqrt{\frac{A}{C_m}}$$

which if $k = \sqrt{\frac{i}{2C_o}}$ is simply another form of the Economic Order Quantity as originally defined in Equation 11.3.

Both *Coverage Analysis* and the original concept of the EOQ appear to produce replenishment order sizes which, in a multi-item inventory situation, creates a reasonably correct product mix in terms of relative orders sizes. Hence it is argued that having established replenishment order sizes on an EOQ principle, all such order sizes could be increased or decreased proportionately based on additional criteria, such as minimizing overall investment, meeting restrictions on storage space and so on.

Questions

1. For a stock control situation, given that the monthly demand is 100 units, and therefore,

   A (annual demand) = 12 × 100 = 1200 units,

   and also the following costs also apply:

   C_o (the cost of raising an order per occasion) = 30;

   i (the annual holding interest rate) = 18 per cent (that is, 0.18);

   and

   C_m (the stocked item's unit value) = 10.00

   what is the Economic Order Quantity?

2. For the situation described in Question 1, what increase in annual operating costs (ordering + storage) occurs if replenishment orders of 400 units (that is, larger than the EOQ) are used? Confirm this increase by calculating costs at both replenishment order sizes.

3. Again for the situation described in Question 1, if replenishment orders of 400 units are used, what minimum discount on purchase price per unit must be achieved for total annual inventory costs (ordering + storage + purchasing/acquisition) to be no higher than those at the EOQ. Again calculate both costs and establish that they are indeed the same.

References and further reading

Eilon, S. 1962, *Elements of Production Planning and Control*. Macmillan, London.

Hill, T. 1983, *Production and Operations Management*. Prentice Hall, New Jersey.

Lewis, C.D. 1998, 'Establishing a Practical Range of Price Discounts that should be Aimed for when purchasing more than the EOQ', *European Journal of Purchasing and Supply Management*, 4, 153 –162.

Lockyer, K., Muhlemann, A. and Oakland, J. 1988, *Production and Operations Management*. Pitman, London.

Makower, M.S. and Williamson, E. 1985, *Teach Yourself OR*, Teach Yourself Books.

Murdoch, J. (ed.) 1981, 'Coverage analysis – a new technique for optimizing the stock ordering policy'. Proceedings of a one day conference held at Cranfield (1965) (Note: As the above reference is no longer available, for details see C.D. Lewis, *Scientific Inventory Control*. Butterworths, 1981, p.148.

Naylor, J. 1996, *Operations Management*. Financial Times/Pitman, London.

Silver, E.A. and Peterson, R. 1985, *Decision Systems for Inventory Management and Production Planning*. Wiley, Chichester.

Urry, S. 1991, *Introductions to Operational Research*. Longman, London.

Waters, C.D.J. 1992, *Inventory Control and Management*. Wiley, Chichester.

Wild, R. 1980, *Essentials of Operations Management*. Holt, Rinehart & Winston, New York.

Wilson, R.H. 1934–5, 'A Scientific Routine for Stock Control', *Harvard Business Review*, 13.

The Re-order Level Inventory Policy: Examining the Relationship between the Re-order Level and the Replenishment Order Size

Introduction

In discussing the traditional methods of establishing the two controlling parameters of the re-order level inventory policy, Chapter 10 considered the setting of the re-order level based on the basis of offering a specified level of service, whereas Chapter 11 considered the evaluation of the replenishment quantity on a totally separate basis of minimizing annual costs of ordering and storage.

In this chapter the relationship of these two controlling parameters is considered.

Interpreting the 'service level' based on simple statistical concepts

For the demand situation considered in Chapter 10, p. 170, a traditional stock control package would evaluate a re-order level of 260 units to offer a 97.7 per cent 'vendor service level' defined as the *probability of not running out of stock on those occasions the policy was at risk of running out*, that is, the probability of a stockout *not* occurring subsequent to an order for replenishment being raised but prior to its being received. As a totally separate exercise, for the costs and demand situation discussed in Chapter 11, p. 177, the replenishment quantity would be calculated as the Economic Order Quantity of 400 units, that is, *that replenishment order size which minimized annual operating costs* such as the costs of ordering and storage.

Although the discussion describing the setting of the re-order level policy's controlling parameters in Chapters 10 and 11 appears logical and conclusive, and was indeed the basis for most stock control packages for many years, it subsequently became apparent that the underlying theory contained three possible flaws, namely:

1. The 'vendor service level' – defined as the *probability of not running out of stock on those occasions the policy was at risk of running out* and evaluated using simple normal probability theory, although appearing to offer a logical approach to establishing the re-order level value, on closer inspection fails to identify either the frequency or severity of stockouts (that is, how often stockouts occur or how many units of unfulfilled demand or stock shortage occur), or to indicate to customers of the stock control system what proportion of their demand would be met ex-stock (that is, immediately). A very simple illustration of this feature would be to consider a probability of not running out of stock per occasion of 11/12 that is, 91.66 per cent which, alternatively offers a probability of stockout of 1/12 that is, 8.34 per cent. At such a level of service, were replenishments to be ordered on a monthly basis, clearly one stockout would occur per year on average. However with larger, quarterly replenishments a stockout would occur once every three years - even though in both cases the 'vendor service level' would be 91.66! Hardly a convincing measure of service for customers.

2. The underlying formula used to calculate the re-order level assumes that when a replenishment order is raised the stock-on-hand exactly equals the re-order level. However, in practice this rarely occurs since in most situations the stock-on-hand will be below the re-order level by an amount known as the 'overshoot' at the instant that the replenishment order is raised. This feature can be confirmed by inspection of Figure 12.1. This displays a simulation of several stock balances in the vicinity of the re-order level together with the amount of overshoot which occurs when each replenishment order is raised. It is interesting to note that overshoot of the re-order level is very rarely zero, even though the calculation of the re-order level has so far been based on the fact that stock balances always equal the re-order level exactly at the instant a new replenishment order is raised, that is, that the overshoot is assumed to be zero.

   The effect of the overshoot clearly means that the effective re-order level at which replenishment orders are on average placed is lower than the nominal re-order level specified originally by

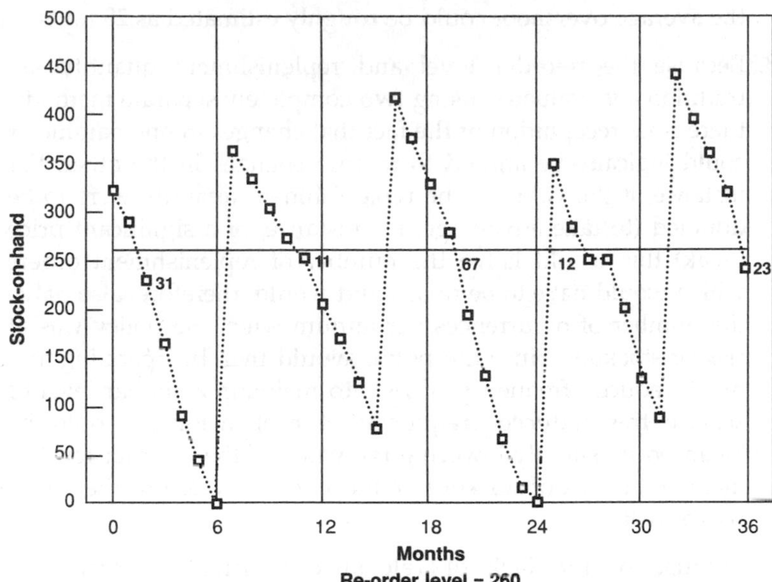

Figure 12.1 Overshoot of re-order level showing that the re-order level is rarely equalled when a replenishment order is raised

Equation 10.1. In an attempt to investigate this effect, for the situation depicted originally in Figure 10.3 and supported in detail in Table 10.1, to establish an estimate of the amount of overshoot it can be seen by examining Table 10.1 that actual 'vendor service level' is lowered from the theoretical level 97.7 per cent, corresponding to a re-order level of 260, to a lower actual simulated level of 87.5 per cent. Much of this actual drop in service level is attributable to the effect of the overshoot, and examination of the Appendix provides a corresponding value of the normal variable $u_{0.125}$ corresponding to a 'vendor service level' of 87.5 per cent, which is 1.15. Substituting this value in Equation 10.1 but using M' as the effective (as opposed to theoretical) re-order level then provides:

$$M' = \bar{D}L + u_{0.125}\,\sigma_d\sqrt{L}$$

$$M' = 50 \times 4 + 1.15 \times 15\sqrt{4} = 235 \text{ units}$$

indicating that the *effective* re-order level offering an actual 'vendor service level' of 87.5 per cent is 235 units, 25 units below the *theoretical* re-order level of 260 units. Hence, in this situation the average overshoot could be roughly estimated as 25 units.

3. Because the re-order level and replenishment quantity are traditionally evaluated using two completely separate methods, there is no recognition of the fact that changes in one parameter could logically be argued to require changes in the other. For instance, if the value of the replenishment quantity were to be doubled (to take advantage, for instance, of a significant price break) this would halve the number of replenishment orders which would have to be raised and would, therefore, also halve the number of occurrences per annum when the policy was at risk of stockout. Since the policy would then be operating at a much reduced frequency of risk, to maintain a similar level of service this reduced frequency of replenishment could be balanced by slightly lowering the value of the re-order level to increase the risk of stockout on those fewer occasions the policy was at risk.

Because of the lack of relevance (particularly from the customer's point-of-view) of the concept of a service level defined as the *probability of not running out of stock on those occasions the policy was at risk of running out*, this particular definition of service has come to be referred to as the 'vendor service level'. The logic for this is that although such a measure of service might mean something to the stockholder (vendor), who may be aware of the size and frequency of replenishment orders, it certainly means little or nothing to the customers of the stockholding system.

'Customer service level' defined as the proportion of annual demand met ex-stock per annum

A more meaningful level of service offered by a stock control system would be the *proportion of annual demand met ex-stock per annum*. Such a measure of service would indicate to the customer of an inventory system the number of demand units per annum which would not be satisfied ex-stock. Such a measure has proved to be far more meaningful than the 'vendor service level' and has, in recent years, been adopted as an alternative and preferable measure of service of a inventory control system.

(Note: Some readers might like to avoid the technical discussion that follows and simply proceed to the conclusion of this analysis as represented by Equation 12.1 on page 195).

To establish theoretically the value of the 'customer service level' it is clearly necessary to establish an estimate of the proportion of annual demand met ex-stock. This is slightly technical but is achieved by considering the right-hand tail of the normal distribution of demand during the lead-time. To demonstrate this for the existing situation where it has now been established that the effective re-order level is only 235 units, Figure 12.2 shows that although the *area* (first integral) to the right of the effective re-order level is (100.0 – 87.5) = 12.5 per cent of the total area of the normal probability curve, conceptually in terms of actual units of demand during the lead-time there must also be an average number of units between this value of 235 and plus infinity. This average number of units, if the value could be evaluated, would represent the average number of units of demand during the lead-time in excess of the effective re-order level, that is, the average number of units of shortage (demand not met ex-stock) subsequent to the placing of a replenishment order. Given that the number of replenishment orders raised per year is known to be equal to $\frac{A}{q}$ (if A is the annual demand and q the replenishment quantity) in addition to the average shortage per occasion, it would then clearly be possible to establish the number of units per annum which would not be available to customers ex-stock.

To calculate the average shortage per occasion, it is necessary to have values of the second integral of the normal probability density function (pdf) between specified limits which would represent the average number of units between those limits. The double (or second) integral of the normal pdf is known as the 'partial expectation' $E(u)$ and, although not published in many sets of statistical tables, values for the (0,1) Normal distribution's 'partial expectation' can be evaluated theoretically and are shown in the Appendix.

Referring firstly to Figure 12.2 and then the Appendix, for the situation currently under consideration, a value of the standard normal variable $u_{0.125} = 1.15$ represents the position of the effective re-order level in terms of standard deviation of demand during the lead-time above the average. Again from the Appendix, the value of the partial expectation corresponding to $u0.125$ produces $E(u) = 0.062$ for the (0,1) Normal distribution. For the actual distribution of demand during the lead-time for the situation under consideration, with a standard deviation $\sigma_d\sqrt{L} = 30$ units it follows that the equivalent value of $E(u)\sigma_d\sqrt{L} = 0.062 \times 30 = 1.86$ units of shortage per occasion implying a shortage would occur. Given that there are

$\frac{A}{q} = 12 \times 50/400 = 1.5$ replenishment orders placed per annum, the annual shortage is given by $1.5 \times 1.67 = 2.79$ units per annum. For an annual demand of $A = 600$ units, a shortage of only 2.79 units means that 597.21 units of demand per annum are met ex-stock thus offering a 'customer service level' defined as *the proportion of annual demand met ex-stock* of $P' = 597.21/600 = 99.5$ per cent.

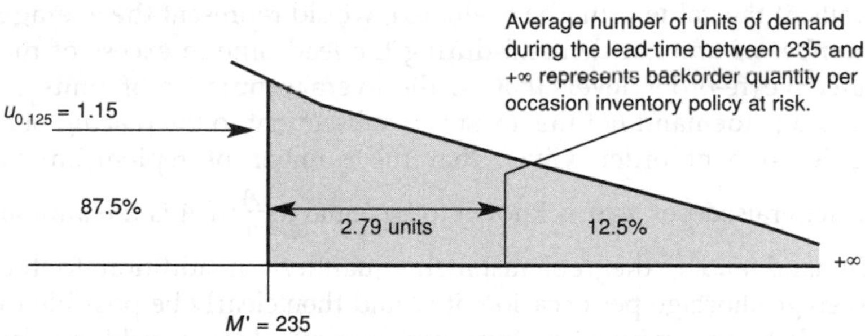

Figure 12.2. Distribution of demand during the lead-time showing the right-hand end of the assumed normal distribution between the effective re-order level $M' = 235$ and $+\infty$ (*plus infinity*)

Summarizing the above discussion in more general terms – see Lewis (1980) – the expected shortage per occasion is given by $E(u)\sigma_d\sqrt{L}$ which for A/q occasions per annum defines the shortage per annum as:

$$\left(\frac{A}{q}\right)E(u)\sigma_d\sqrt{L}.$$

If the 'customer service level' P' is defined as the proportion of annual demand met ex-stock, the defined expected shortage per annum is given by:

$$(1 - P')A.$$

Equating the two produces:

$$(1 - P')A = \left(\frac{A}{q}\right)E(u)\sigma_d\sqrt{L}$$

which allows the 'customer service level' P' to be defined by:

$$P' = 1 - \frac{E(u)\sigma_d\sqrt{L}}{q}. \quad (12.1)$$

Equation 12.1 not only produces a much more meaningful measure of service but also permits the two controlling parameters of the re-order level policy, the re-order level and the replenishment order quantity, to be evaluated jointly.

For instance, if a value of 'customer service level' P' is stipulated (on the assumption that the proportion of annual demand met ex-stock is a more meaningful measure of service offered by a stock control system) and the value of q is specified (on the assumption that with a flexible choice of the replenishment order size the stock-holder has a better chance of reducing costs per unit), with the value standard deviation of demand per period σ_d and value of the lead-time L specified, it follows that by transposing Equation 12.1 the 'partial expectation' E(u) can be evaluated using:

$$E(u) = \frac{q(1 - P')}{\sigma_d\sqrt{L}}. \quad (12.2)$$

With a value of E(u), the normal variable u can be established from the Appendix and, hence the re-order level M calculated using Equation 10.1. Thus the values of both parameters controlling the re-order level policy would have been evaluated jointly.

To confirm the validity of Equation 12.1, where it was originally assumed that a re-order level of 260 units offered a 'vendor service level' of 97.7 per cent with the normal variable $u_{0.02275} = 2$ and the 'partial expectation' $E(u) = 0.008$ from the Appendix, then substituting in Equation 12.1 provides:

$$P' = 1 - 0.008 \times 15\sqrt{4}/400 = 99.9 \text{ per cent.}$$

This produces a rather ironic situation in which, in terms that the customer really wouldn't understand, an original service level offer by the vendor (or stock holder) of 97.7 per cent (that is, 'vendor service level') would produce a much lower actual value of 87.5 per cent. However, in terms the customer would understood, such as proportion of annual demand met ex-stock (that is, 'customer service level') a significantly better level of service of 99.9 per cent would be experienced!

Conclusion

Conventional wisdom requires that a measure of service be specified for a stock control system from which the value of the parameters controlling that system can then be established. By specifying a relatively high value of 'vendor service level', defined as the *probability of not running out of stock on those occasions the policy was at risk of running out* in practice, because of the overshoot of the re-order level a much lower level of service is offered. However, customers' perception of service is measured in terms of the *proportion of demand met-ex-stock per annum* and it can be shown that this measure of 'customer service level' is always much higher than the value of 'vendor service level'.

Thus, although the stockholder (or 'vendor') offers customers nowhere near as high a service level as specified, in terms that customers understand they actually receive a higher level of service. Perhaps this is perhaps one of those rare circumstances where several wrongs make a right!

Question

1. For the demand and lead-time situation described in Question 1, Chapter 10, what 'vendor service level' and 'customer service level' would be offered when operating at a re-order level of 682 units and a replenishment order size of 1000 units if the average overshoot is assumed to be 25.5 units?

References and further reading

Bolton, W. 1994, *Production Planning and Control*. Longman, Harlow.
Hill, T. 1983, *Production and Operations Management*. Prentice Hall, New Jersey.
Lewis, C.D. 1980, *Scientific Inventory Control*. Butterworths, London.
Lockyer, K., Muhlemann, A. and Oakland, J. 1988, *Production and Operations Management*. Pitman, London.
Urry, S. 1991, *Introductions to Operational Research*. Longman, Harlow.
Wild, R. 1980, *Essentials of Operations Management*. Holt, Rinehart & Winston, New York.
Waters, C.D.J. 1992, *Inventory Control and Management*. Wiley, Chichester.

The Re-order Cycle Inventory Policy: Establishing the Value of the Review Period and the Maximum Stock Level

Introduction

The re-order cycle inventory policy (sometimes known as the periodic review system), is the next most commonly used inventory control policy after the re-order level policy. This inventory policy operates on the basis that replenishment orders of a variable size are placed at regular intervals of time *R*. When a replenishment order is raised, it is calculated as that size of order which would bring the stock balances up to a maximum level *S* if replenishment were instantaneous (that is, if the lead-time was zero). This ensures that when stock-on-hand (physical stock held plus outstanding replenishments less committed stock) is low at review, a relatively large replenishment order is placed. Conversely, when stock-on-hand is high at review, a relatively small replenishment order is placed. Thus the re-ordering process attempts to keep stock balances stable even though, when the size of the replenishment order is established at each review, stock balances may be at very different levels.

One of the major advantages of this policy is that orders for replenishment are placed at regular intervals, which allows for multiple item orders on individual suppliers (that is, one order for several different items on the same supplier). Also, with such regular replenishment, better and more even planning of the replenishment ordering process can be implemented. Hence, it is generally assumed that the costs of raising individual replenishment orders on suppliers within the re-order cycle policy are cheaper than when operating a re-order level policy.

Selecting the review period in the re-order cycle inventory policy

The re-order cycle policy is controlled entirely by the review period R and the maximum stock level S. On each occasion the stock-on-hand is reviewed after a period equal to R time units, a replenishment order equal to the maximum stock level S less the current level of stock is placed. This means that, as with the re-order level policy, the re-order cycle policy is controlled by just two parameters, namely R and S. However, because the review period R is a measure of time duration, it is often chosen on an arbitrary basis to fit in with a wider time framework and is usually chosen to be equal to a standard time unit, such as a day, week, calendar month (or planning period), quarter (three months) or even a year.

To establish the desired length of the review period, theoretically it is possible to use an approach similar to that used in Chapter 11 to formulate the 'Economic Order Quantity' and within this re-order cycle policy establish m_o, the 'economic number of reviews per annum' and from this establish that 'economic review period' R_o which would minimise the annual operating costs.

A similar approach (see page 175) for formulating the annual inventory operating costs C_A for the re-order cycle policy, in terms of the costs of ordering replenishment orders and costs of storage per annum, to establish the value of the 'Economic Review Period' R_o would suggest that:

- Ordering costs (that is, costs of raising replenishment orders) per annum are assumed to be equal to the number of reviews per year m multiplied by the cost C_o of raising each individual order; where C_o is again assumed to be independent of the order sizes, that is, mC_o.
- Storage costs per annum are assumed to be based on the average level of stock held, this latter being evaluated as where $\left(\frac{A}{2m} + s\right)$ represents half the average replenishment order (A being the annual demand and m the number of reviews per annum) and s is again the fixed value of safety stock (that is, independent of the number of reviews per year m). The annual costs of storage are then established as this average stock level multiplied by the

unit cost of storage per annum iC_m to produce $\left(\frac{A}{2m} + s\right) iC_m$.

It then follows that if the annual costs C_A of operating an inventory policy can be assumed to be equal to the costs of ordering replenishments plus the costs of storage, then:

$$C_A = mC_o + \left(\frac{A}{2m} + s\right) iC_m \tag{13.1}$$

where:

m is the number of reviews made per year,
C_o is the cost of raising an individual replenishment order (say 30),
A is annual demand $A = 12\bar{D}$ (say $12 \times 50 = 600$),
s is the fixed safety stock whose size is independent of m,
iC_m is the annual unit storage cost, with the unit storage cost, where i is expressed as a percentage of C_m, the stocked item's value (unit material cost). With i set at 22.5 per cent p.a., and C_m at 1.00 this produces annual unit storage cost $0.225 \times 1.00 = 0.225$.

Differentiating the annual operating cost C_A (as defined by Equation 13.1) with respect to the number of reviews m, defines $\frac{dC_A}{dm}$ as:

$$\frac{dC_A}{dm} = C_o - \frac{(AiC_m)}{2m^2}. \tag{13.2}$$

Hence, the optimal frequency of placing replenishment orders which minimizes the annual operating cost, is then defined by $\frac{dC_A}{dm} = 0$, from which the 'economic number of reviews per annum' m_o is defined as:

$$m_o = \sqrt{\frac{AiC_m}{2C_o}} \tag{13.3}$$

Where the period of time (or time unit) on which the demand average and standard deviation are based and also the lead-time is measured is calendar months, the review period R_o which minimises the annual operating cost based on a twelve month year is given by:

$$R_o = \frac{12}{m_o} = \frac{12}{\sqrt{\frac{AiC_m}{2C_o}}} \quad (13.4)$$

which, for the situation under consideration produces:

$$R_o = \frac{12}{\sqrt{\frac{600 \times 0.225 \times 1.00}{2 \times 30}}}$$

$$R_o = 8 \text{ months.}$$

It should be noted that the value of R_o developed using this approach should only be regarded as an indication as to the appropriate review period. For practical reasons the choice of a review period for a re-order cycle policy will invariably tend to be a multiple of a standard unit of time such as a day, week, month (planning period), year, and so on.

Setting the maximum stock level

Figure 13.1 shows simulated stock balances for a re-order cycle policy over an initial three year period and indicates when orders for replenishment are raised (ord) – at regular intervals of time (every eight months) – and subsequently received (rec) after the lead-time delay, which in this particular situation is set at four months. The size of the replenishment order is calculated as a maximum stock level S (=704 units) less the stock-on-hand at each review.

For the three year period shown here, an eight month review period combined with a maximum stock level value of 704 units appears to achieve a reasonable balance as, on the one hand no stockouts occur during the three years being considered and on the other, unused stock (the gap between minimum stocks and zero stock) is never excessively high.

Examination of Figure 13.1 confirms that the operation of the re-order cycle inventory control policy is determined completely by the setting of just two parameters, namely the value of the review period R and the value of the maximum stock level S used in the calculation of the replenishment quantity.

Examining in detail the stock balances for the re-order cycle policy as shown in Figure 13.1, it should be noted that the decision to place a replenishment order (indicated by ord) at position ***A*** (month 0) with regard to the possibility of stockout occurring prior to the receipt of the replenishment order (indicated by rec) affects the outcome at position ***C*** (month 12) rather than the closer position ***B*** (month 4). This is because the outcome at position ***C***, in terms of a potential stockout, is clearly a function of the stock held at position at ***B'***. But the amount of stock held at this position at ***B'*** is in turn dependent on the decision as to whether to place a large or small replenishment order at the previous review; which occurred at position ***A*** and which was received at position ***B***.

Since the positions ***A*** and ***C*** are separated by (R + L) months or time periods, this time duration (R + L) can be interpreted as the period of risk for the re-order cycle policy which, in the case under consideration here, is 8 + 4 = 12.

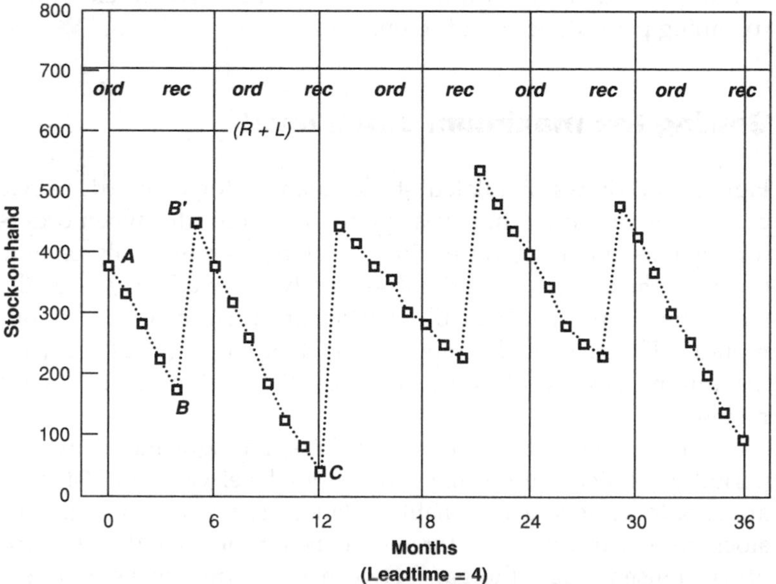

Figure 13.1 Re-order cycle policy stock balances for three-year period

If it is accepted that $(R + L)$ be regarded as the period of risk for a re-order cycle policy and if the maximum stock level S can be regarded as equivalent to a re-order level which stock balances are always below, then Equation 10.1 (see page 169) – originally proposed for establishing the value of the re-order level within a re-order level policy – can now be modified to establish the value of the maximum stock level S within a re-order cycle policy by replacing M with S and L with $(R + L)$ such that:

$$S = \bar{D}(R + L) + u_{0.02275}\, \sigma_d \sqrt{R + L}\,. \qquad (13.5)$$

For the demand situation dealt with previously with $\bar{D} = 50$, $\sigma_d = 15$, $L = 4$ and with now in addition the review period $R = 8$, for a 97.7 per cent 'vendor service level' – *probability of not running out of stock on those occasions the policy is at risk of running out* – for which the normal variable $u_{0.02275} = 2$ from the Appendix, the maximum stock level S developed from Equation 13.5 would produce a value of 704 units as shown below:

$$S = 50 \times (8 + 4) + 2 \times 15 \times \sqrt{8 + 4} = 600 + 104$$
$$S = 704 \text{ units.}$$

Table 13.1 shows, in numerical form, the stock balances for the first twelve months for the situation shown previously in Figure 13.1. Examining the detail of this table shows that the stock balances have resulted from a situation where:

- The demand per unit time was specified to be distributed normally with an average $\bar{D} = 50$ units/month and a standard deviation $\sigma_d = 15$ units/month whereas the average values actually generated by the simulation model for this particular sequence were only marginally different at 48.66 and 15.01 respectively;
- The duration of the lead-time delay in obtaining replenishments was fixed at $L = 4$ months;
- The review period was set at $R = 8$ months, and
- The maximum stock level S was set at 704 as defined by Equation 13.5 and the calculation of the two replenishment orders placed during this year are both indicated.

This relationship, between the review period R and maximum

COSTS:

Storage (% p.a. mat'l cost)	22.50%
Material (+ lab + o'heads)	1.00
Ordering cost/occasion	30.00
Penalty cost/period	30.00

PARAMETERS:	***Specified***	***Theoretical***
Re-order level	704	704
Replenishment quantity	361	NA
Vendor service level	100.0%	97.7%
Customer service level	100.0%	99.7%

DEMAND/ MONTH	***Specified***	***Actual***
Average	50.00	49.46
Std. deviation	15.00	15.66
Review/Leadtime	8	4
STOCKTURN		**1.99**

SIMULATED COSTS/ANNUM

Storage costs	64.88
Ordering costs	45.00
Penalty costs	00.00
Total operating costs	**109.88**

Months	**Previous stock**	**Current demand**	**Received orders**	**Stock-on- hand**	**Size of replenishment order placed (fixed)**
0	385***A***	554		330	374
1	330	50		280	*= (704 – 330)*
2	280	51		229	
3	229	70		159	
4	159***B***	56	374	477***B'***	
5	477	60		417	
6	417	51		366	
7	366	80		286	
8	286	62		224	480
9	224	47		177	*= (704 – 224)*
10	177	41		136	
11	136	60		76	
12	76	36		40***C***	

Table 13.1 Table of simulated stock balances for a re-order cycle policy subject to demand situation where average demand ($\overline{D}$) = 50 and standard deviation of demand (σ_d) = 15 with a lead-time of 4 and a review period of 8. The actual maximum stock level controlling the simulation is set equal to the theoretical value of 704 computed using Equation 7.5.

stock level S, in maintaining reasonable stock balances for the situation under consideration can be seen in Figure 13.2 which shows the complete 12 years simulation of stock balances for the re-order cycle policy operating with a review period of eight months and a maximum stock level of 704. This gives a longer, overall picture of the stock balances and confirms that this combination of values does appear to offer a good solution.

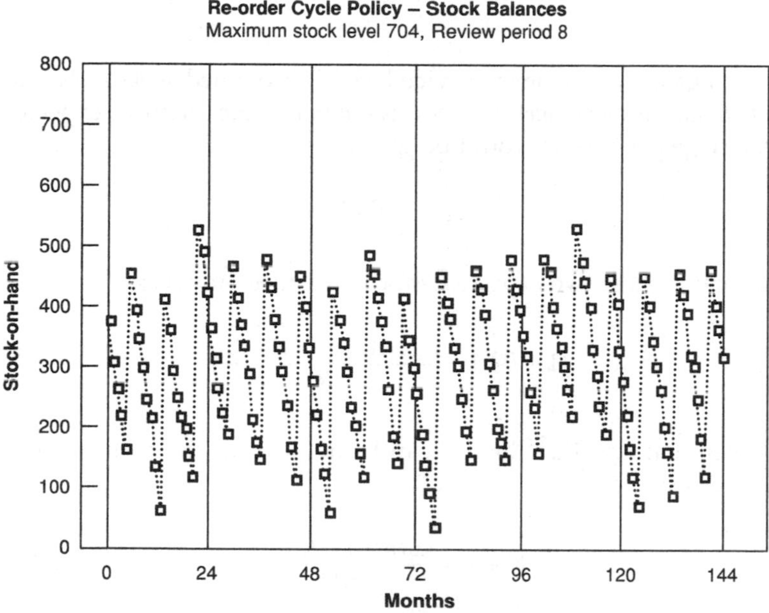

Figure 13.2 Re-order cycle policy stock balances for twelve-year period

Establishing the 'customer service level' defined as the proportion of annual demand met ex-stock per annum within a re-order cycle policy

(Note: Some readers might like to avoid the technical discussion that follows and simply proceed to the conclusion of this analysis as represented by Equation 13.6 on page 206).

Using similar arguments as established previously for the re-order level policy (see page 190), in the case of the re-order cycle policy situation being considered here, the period of risk for this policy is $(R + L)$ and the policy is at risk of a possible stockout after the placing of $m = 12/R$ replenishment orders being placed per annum. Given that the expected shortage per occasion is $E(u)\sigma_d\sqrt{R + L}$, where $E(u)$ is the partial expectation of the normal distribution, the expected shortage per annum would be given by:

$$\left(\frac{12E(u)\sigma_d\sqrt{R+L}}{R}\right).$$

If again the 'customer service level' P' is defined as *the proportion of annual demand met ex-stock per annum,* the defined expected shortage per annum would be given by:

$$(1 - P')A.$$

Equating these two expected shortage values produces:

$$(1 - P')A = \left(\frac{12E(u)\sigma_d\sqrt{R+L}}{R}\right).$$

Given that $A = 12\bar{D}$, then P' can be defined for the re-order cycle policy as:

$$P' = 1 - \frac{E(u)\sigma_d\sqrt{R+L}}{RD}. \tag{13.6}$$

With the appropriate value of $E(u)$ for $u_{0.02275}$ of 0.008 from the Appendix (there being no overshoot effect to consider in the re-order cycle policy), for the situation under consideration P' is evaluated as:

$$P' = 1 - \frac{0.008 \times 15\sqrt{8+4}}{8 \times 50} = 0.9989,$$

offering a theoretical 'customer service level' of 99.89 per cent.

It should be noted that, as with the re-order level policy, the 'customer service level' for the re-order cycle policy is always higher than the 'vendor service level'.

Conclusion

The setting of the review period R within a re-order cycle policy will usually be on the basis of choosing a time period which fits within an overall time framework. However, by adopting an approach similar to the 'Economic Order Quantity' approach discussed in Chapter 12, it is possible to show that the value of an 'economic review period' can be established. Such a review period value should be considered as only indicative, since in practice as a time duration it will always be more convenient to choose a standard unit of time such as a week, month (or planning period), year, and so on.

Having specified the review period for the re-order cycle policy, the remaining parameter which controls the operation of the policy is the maximum stock level S which is used to calculate the size of replenishment orders at each review. This value of the maximum stock level can be established using a 'vendor service level' approach. Subsequent considerations show that the 'customer service level' will be higher than the 'vendor service level'. Also, because there are no 'overshoot' effects in this policy, the actual 'customer service level' and 'vendor service level' will be much nearer to the theoretical values.

Question

1. For the demand and lead-time situation described in Question 1, Chapter 10, what 'vendor service level' and 'customer service level' would be offered when operating a re-order cycle policy with a maximum stock level S of 3800 units and a review period R of 10 weeks?

Further reading

Hill, T, 1983, *Production and Operations Management*. Prentice Hall, New Jersey.

Lockyer, K., Muhlemann, A. and Oakland, J. 1988, *Production and Operations Management*. Pitman, London.

Urry, S. 1991, *Introductions to Operational Research*. Longman, Harlow.

Wild, R. 1980, *Essentials of Operations Management*. Holt, Rinehart & Winston, New York..

Pareto or ABC Analysis: A Vehicle for Inventory Policy Allocation

Introduction

It is a fact of life that in any system not all items are of equal importance. Pareto's early social commentary in the eighteenth century that 'the majority of Italy's wealth was owned by a minority of its people' is replicated in many situations today. This so called 'Pareto rule' is often described as a 20/80 relationship, which might be translated in a sales situation as '20 per cent of the product lines represent 80 per cent of the sales'.

More particularly, students might like to ponder as to how Union or Guild bar sales are distributed amongst the student population. A possible scenario, which most observers might not find too unfair, would be to conclude that:

- A large proportion of students never visit the Union or Guild much less generate significant sales at the bar.
- A small proportion of students tend to monopolize the bar and, as a result, generate the majority of the bar's sales turnover.
- Somewhere between these groups, a significant although not a major proportion of the student population visit the Union or Guild bar occasionally and although they generate some bar sales, compared with the group that tend to monopolize the bar, their proportion of bar sales turnover is smaller.

Most readers, while accepting the above scenario and its three identifiable groups, would have more difficulty estimating the exact proportions of the student population which fall into the three groups and the proportion of bar turnover each group might generate. However, within an inventory control situation concerned with the stocking of many parts or services, there is a strong and long observed relationship between the distribution of parts or services and the amount they contribute to either stocked value (that is, the average value of stock held) or annual sales turnover. This has led to the definition of three distinct groups, which have been broadly characterized as:

- 'The important few'
- 'The less important', and
- 'The unimportant many'

although it should be pointed out that when it comes to inventory systems and stocked items, no parts or services are completely unimportant.

The exact proportions of parts or services which might fall into the three categories or groups and the exact proportion of stocked value (or alternatively annual sales) each group contributes will depend on the type of company or organization involved and the type of goods or services they deal with. Indeed some authors have even argued that a company can be identified by the shape of its Pareto curve (see Figure 14.2).

However, with the advent of computers and in particular the ability of computers to sort large amounts of information very quickly, this Pareto relationship is readily identifiable and well understood both in industry and commerce, and has for several decades been a basis for choosing how to control parts or services on a basis of 'management by exception'.

Traditionally, parts lists for parts held in stock have been kept in alphabetic order of part-number. This allows anyone with a specific part-number and a rudimentary knowledge of the alphabet, to locate and identify a required part-number even within a list of many thousands. Table 14.1 displays the first twenty parts of such a list which in total contains several thousand parts and shows:

- The part-number;
- The quantity held in stock;
- The average unit costs (most stock control packages allow for the fact that prices for the same stocked item may vary);
- The value of stock at average cost, and
- The cumulative value of stock held (at average cost).

Clearly in this situation, the parts are held in alphabetic order of part-number.

Figure 14.1 displays the plot of percentage cumulative value versus percentage number of parts for all the parts contained in a typical list of several thousand part-numbers, the first 20 of which

Table 14.1 The first 20 part-numbers of a typical parts list sorted in alphabetical order of part-number and containing several thousand parts

	Part-# number	Quantity held in stock	Average unit cost	Value of stock at average cost	Cumulative value of stock held
1	ABC1432	700	34.20	23 940.00	23 940.00
2	ABC1433	700	34.00	23 800.00	47 740.00
3	ACR8907	70 000	0.34	23 800.00	71 540.00
4	ACR8914	70 000	0.67	46 900.00	118 440.00
5	ADE454	8638	4.00	34 552.00	152 992.00
6	ADE565	5355	5.00	26 775.00	179 767.00
7	ADE676	10 500	2.00	21 000.00	200 767.00
8	ADG765	1306	58.00	75 759.60	276 526.60
9	ADR4545	10 500	2.00	21 000.00	297 526.60
10	ADR876	19 593	3.00	58 779.00	356 305.60
11	AFB653	1400	34.00	47 600.00	403 905.60
12	AGR876	19 593	4.00	78 372.00	482 277.60
13	AGT3545	1306	54.00	70 534.80	552 812.40
14	ATF5432	2800	9.00	25 200.00	578 012.40
15	AXT65309	84 000	0.30	25 200.00	603 212.40
16	AYF6574	315	2.00	630.00	603 842.40
17	AZG8743	840	5.00	4200.00	608 042.40
18	BGT5656	861	7.00	6027.00	614 069.40
19	BGT6512	21 770	2.60	56 602.00	670 671.40
20	BHI787	4200	0.70	2940.00	673 611.40

are shown in Table 14.1. If all parts were of equal value, clearly this plot would be a straight, diagonal line. In the more realistic situation where the value of parts and the quantity held in stock vary, as one would expect the plot approximates to a straight, diagonal line with the occasional large valued item (which may be a combination of a few units held in stock of a very valuable items or many units of stock held for a moderately valuable item) causing significant deviations.

Although alphabetic listings are traditional, today, given the computer's ability to sort by any specific field, it is a simple matter to present parts or services listed in any order that might be useful, and particularly in descending order of value (in this case in value of stock at average cost). Table 14.2 demonstrates this by showing the first twenty parts of the same parts list as originally considered in Table 14.1, but this time listed in descending order of value.

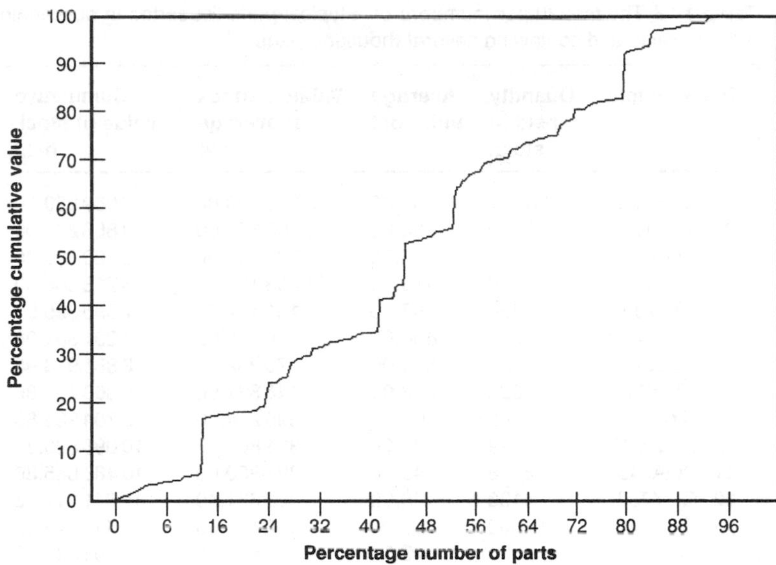

Figure 14.1 Demonstrating the relationship between parts held in stock and their proportion of stock value when parts are listed alphabetically in part-number order

While Table 14.2 does not look dramatically different to Table 14.1, the plot of percentage cumulative value versus percentage number of parts, as shown in Figure 14.2, does display a strong relationship compared with that shown earlier in Figure 14.1. This shows that once it is possible to sort parts by value rather than part-number, the relationship that:

- 10 to 20 per cent of the items listed represent of the order of 80 per cent of the total value. These items are universally referred to as 'A' type items.
- 20 to 30 per cent of the items listed represent about 15 to 20 per cent of the total value. These items are universally referred to as 'B' type items.
- 50 to 70 per cent of the items listed only represent about 5 to 10 per cent of the total value. These items are universally referred to as 'C' type items.

Figure 14.2 graphically demonstrates the relationship between stocked items and their contribution to value which appears

Table 14.2 The first 20 part-numbers of a typical parts list sorted in descending order of value and containing several thousand parts

Part-# number		Quantity held in stock	Average unit cost	Value of stock at average cost	Cumulative value of stock held
1	DDH098	26 124	80.00	2 089 920.00	2 089 920.00
2	JXC0987	3919	450.00	1 763 370.00	3 853 290.00
3	FYD098	17 416	90.00	1 567 440.00	5 420 730.00
4	GHY67676	11 756	110.00	1 293 138.00	6 713 868.00
5	FRT789	17 634	67.00	1 181 457.90	7 895 325.90
6	DOL9432	827	600.00	496 356.00	8 391 681.90
7	KYU8989	784	600.00	470 232.00	8 861 913.90
8	FTR7878	823	543.00	446 837.96	9 308 751.86
9	HYU78787	3962	100.00	396 214.00	9 704 965.86
10	JFG0987	3919	100.00	391 860.00	10 096 825.86
11	DQA5454	8708	45.00	391 860.00	10 488 685.86
12	GHY787	4136	78.00	322 631.40	10 811 317.26
13	EFT6543	13 062	23.00	300 426.00	11 111 743.26
14	FER5454	6531	45.00	293 895.00	11 405 638.26
15	DYT9432	823	345.00	283 902.57	11 689 540.83
16	SER54545	13 106	20.00	262 110.80	11 951 651.63
17	HGT6543	13 062	20.00	261 240.00	12 212 891.63
18	GTY7676	6531	34.00	222 054.00	12 434 945.63
19	GJY0987	7402	23.00	170 241.40	12 605 187.03
20	GFT5654	52 248	3.00	156 744.00	12 761 931.03

throughout industry and commerce when related to parts and services and which has become known variously as:

- Pareto analysis
- ABC analysis, or
- The 80/20 rule,

within which:

- 'A' type items represent the few, but important, items which constitute the major portion of the total value (say 80 per cent);
- 'B' type items, which are usually more numerous than 'A' type items but which do not represent anywhere as near as much in terms of total value, (say 15 per cent), and
- 'C' type items, which represent the vast majority in terms of numbers but only a small percentage of total value (say 5 per cent).

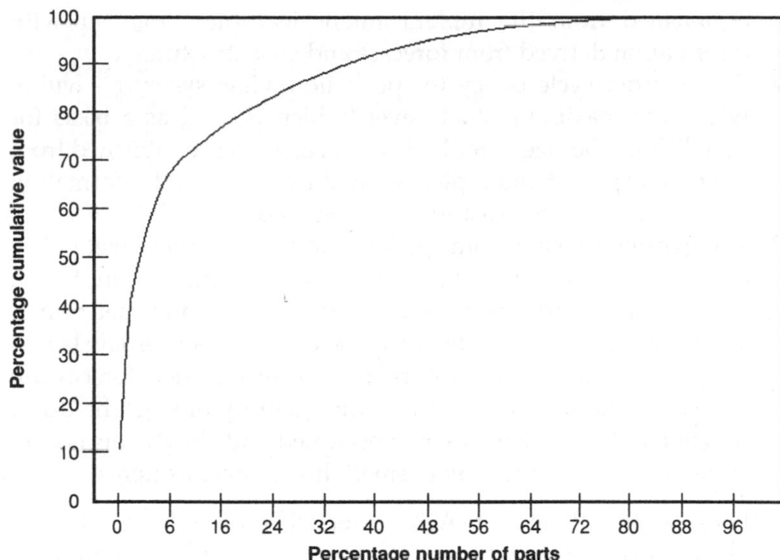

Figure 14.2 Demonstrating the relationship between parts held in stock and their proportion of stock value when parts are listed in descending order of value of stock at average cost

Although in the case discussed here the importance of an item has been equated as its value as stocked, other measures which could be used are:

- Annual sales, and
- Profit contribution.

Management by exception applied to stocked parts

Within any inventory control system involving many stocked items, in view of the earlier discussion, it is clearly not sensible to treat all stocked items as being equally important in terms of selection of an appropriate inventory control policy.

In terms of that selection, there are essentially three options on offer, namely:

1. The re-order level policy (or fixed order quantity system) – within which the re-order level and replenishment quantity are

established from the replenishment lead-time together with information derived from forecast and cost structure;

2. The re-order cycle policy (or periodic review system) – within which the maximum stock level (which is used as a basis for establishing the size of replenishment orders) is established from the review period and replenishment lead-time and information derived from the forecast information, and
3. The two-bin (or single bin) policy, that is, a re-order level policy operated on the basis that when the first bin is emptied a replenishment order is placed and further demand met from a second bin whose size effectively becomes a re-order level. This inventory policy does not require a formalized forecasting procedure but does assume that the quantity of stock held is a function of the volume of space occupied and clearly this is only likely to be true for relatively small, homogeneous items.

Because the Pareto or ABC categorization scheme divides stocked items into *three* types 'A', 'B' and 'C' and there are *three* inventory control systems on offer, this is suggested as a categorisation system for recommending which type of stock control policy is most appropriate for each type of stocked item.

Selection of inventory control policy based on type of stocked item as derived from Pareto analysis

Allocation of inventory control policy(ies) to 'A' and 'B' items

Because there does not appear to be a significant advantage in allocating either the re-order level or re-order cycle policy to either 'A' or 'B' items, the general recommendation would be that since both 'A' and 'B' items are clearly of significant importance (relative to 'C' items), items in these two groups should be controlled by a well specified inventory control policy linked to a formalized forecasting procedure. Equally it might well be acceptable that 'C' items, being more numerous and less important, could be controlled by a less well specified inventory control policy with no link to a formalized forecasting procedure.

In attempting to be more specific as to which of the two major inventory control policies is more appropriate for 'A' and 'B' type items, Waters (1992) has indicated that

> The main benefit of a periodic review system (re-order cycle policy) is that it is simple and convenient to administer. There is a routine where stock is checked at regular times, orders are placed, delivery is arranged, goods arriving are checked, and so on. This is particularly useful for cheap items with high demand. The routine also means that the stock level is only checked at specific intervals and does not have to be monitored continuously.

In addition to this argument, the re-order cycle policy because of its longer period of risk compared with the re-order level policy, tends to hold more stock for the same level of service.

This can be measured by 'stockturn or turnover' which can be defined as:

$$\text{Stock turnover} = \frac{\text{Annual turnover}}{\text{Average stock held}}$$

which measures how often in a year the average value of stock held is issued or 'turned over'. In general stockturn will be lower for the re-order cycle policy (see Table 13.1, page 204 where stockturn = 1.99) compared with the re-order level policy (see Table 10.1, page 170 where stockturn = 2.79).

On the basis that 'B' items are cheaper than 'A' items, Waters' argument, and that based on stockturn, would suggest that on balance 'B' items should be controlled by the re-order cycle policy.

With regard to the re-order level policy, Waters argues that:

> a major advantage of the fixed order quantity systems (i.e. re-order level policy) is that orders of a constant size are easier to regulate than variables ones. Suppliers know how much to send and the administration and transportation can be tailored to specific needs (perhaps supplying a truck load at a time). Also a fixed order system has more flexibility to suit order frequency to demand.

Such advantages might indicate that the re-order level policy is marginally more suitable for 'A' items. This assertion could be said to have added emphasis now that one of the basic criticisms of the re-order level policy of not being able to identify items which were rapidly becoming obsolete has been overcome by computerization. This criticism used to be levelled at the re-order level policy on the basis that with little or no demand, re-order levels were not broken and, therefore no message emanated from the system indicating that demand for the item had nearly ceased. All computerized inventory control systems are now capable of producing exception reports for slow movers such that this inability to identify potentially obsolete items simply because re-order levels were not being broken should no longer be a significant problem associated specifically with this policy.

Allocation of inventory control policy to 'C' items

In considering the most appropriate inventory control approach which could be associated with 'C' items, the fact that 'C' items represent the majority of items in stock control systems but a very small proportion of overall value, must raise the issue of whether a formalized inventory control system is appropriate for these items at all. Because these items represent such a small proportion of the value invested in stocked items but a large proportion of the actual number, it may be sensible in practice to control these items simply by overstocking. In approximate terms 20 per cent overstocking of 5 per cent of the investment in stocked parts only incurs an approximate cost of 1 per cent overall. If the cost of both a formalized forecasting system, and the cost of the subsequent linking of information derived from the forecasts to establish the correct parameters of either a re-order level or re-order cycle inventory policy, is greater than the 1 per cent of stock investment for these 'C' items – it could well be that an alternative approach should be considered.

Such an approach could be the so called *two-bin* policy which is effectively a re-order level policy within which;

- Parts are held in two bins (or one bin with a marked level);
- It is assumed that parts are relatively small and homogeneous such that it can be assumed that the number of parts held can be assumed to be a function of the volume occupied;
- There is no formalized forecasting system, and
- Replenishment orders are raised when the first bin is emptied (or parts fall below the marked level in a single bin, see page 171) both being regarded as being equivalent to the re-order level.

Conclusion

This chapter has discussed the suitability of different inventory control system for different types of stocked items and has argued that ABC or Pareto analysis is the most appropriate categorization or grouping system to use. Although it is not absolutely clear-cut as to which of the re-order level or re-order cycle policies is more appropriate for either 'A' or 'B' items, clearly the relative importance of these items suggests that both types should be controlled by a formalized inventory control system linked to a formalized forecasting system (to provide an analysis of demand). On balance it has been argued that 'A' type items should be controlled by a re-order level policy and 'B' type items by a re-order cycle policy.

For 'C' items it is argued that on a cost benefit approach it might be sensible to stock the many but relatively unimportant items using a *two-bin* inventory control system and not employing a formalized forecasting system at all.

References and further reading

Buchan, J., and Koenigsberg, E. 1963, *Scientific inventory management*. Prentice Hall, NJ.

Bolton, W. 1994, *Production Planning and Control*. Longman, Harlow.

Burbidge, J.L. 1962, *The principles and practice of production control*. Macdonald, London.

Eppen, G.D. Gould, F.J. and Schmidt, C.P. 1993, *Introductory Management Science*. Prentice Hall, NJ.

Gordon, G. Pressman, I. and Cohen, S. 1990, *Quantitative Decision Making for Business*. Prentice Hall, NJ.

Hill, T. 1983, *Production and Operations Management*. Prentice Hall, NJ.

Lockyer, K. Muhlemann, A. and Oakland, J. 1988, *Production and Operations Management*. Pitman. London.

Lucey, T. 1988, *Quantitative Techniques*. DP Publications, London.

Makower, M.S. and Williamson, E. 1985, *Teach Yourself OR*. Teach Yourself Books, London.

Naylor, J. 1996, *Operations Management*. Financial Times/Pitman, London.

Urry, S. 1991, *Introductions to Operational Research*. Longman, Harlow.

Waters, C.D.J. 1992, *Inventory Control and Management*. Wiley, Chichester.

Wild, R. 1980, *Essentials of Operations Management*. Holt, Rinehart & Winston, New York.

Appendix

Selected values of normal variable *u*

Probability of *u* not being exceeded (vendor service level per cent), Probability of *u* being exceeded (probability of stockout per cent), and Partial expectation *E*(*u*).

Normal Variable (*u*)	Vendor Service Level (%)	Probability of Stockout %	Partial Expectation *E*(*u*)
0.60	72.6	27.4	0.169
0.70	75.8	24.2	0.143
0.80	78.8	21.2	0.120
0.90	81.6	18.4	0.100
1.00	84.1	15.9	0.083
1.05	85.3	14.7	0.076
1.10	86.4	13.6	0.069
1.15	87.5	12.5	0.062
1.20	88.5	11.5	0.056
1.25	89.4	10.6	0.051
1.30	90.0	10.0	0.046
1.35	91.2	8.8	0.041
1.40	91.9	8.1	0.037
1.45	92.7	7.3	0.033
1.50	93.3	6.7	0.029
1.55	94.0	6.0	0.026
1.60	94.5	5.5	0.023
1.65	95.1	4.9	0.021
1.70	95.5	4.5	0.018
1.75	96.0	4.0	0.016
1.80	96.4	3.6	0.014
1.85	96.8	3.2	0.013
1.90	97.1	2.9	0.011
1.95	97.4	2.6	0.010
2.00	97.7	2.3 (2.275)	0.008
2.25	98.8	1.2	0.004
2.50	99.4	0.2	0.002
2.75	99.7	0.3	0.001
3.00	99.9	0.1	0.000

Answers to Questions

Chapter 8

Question 1. The completed table should appear as the rows 1 to 4 as shown below

Chapter 9

QUESTION 1. The completed table should appear as rows 5 to 9 as shown below

		Jan	Feb	Mar	Apr	May	Jun
1	**Current period's demand** d_t	123	100	178	122	86	52
2	**Current period's forecast** $f_t = u_{t-1}$	100	105	104	119	120	113
3	**Current period's forecast error** $e_t = d_t - f_t$	23	–5	74	3	–34	–61
4	**One period ahead forecast** $f_{t+1} = u_t = \alpha d_t + (1 - \alpha) u_{t-1}$	105	104	119	120	113	101
5	**Squared Error** e_t^2	529	25	5476	9	1156	3721
6	**Absolute Percentage Error** APE = $100\ \lvert e_t \rvert / d_t$	*19%*	*5%*	*42%*	*2%*	*40%*	*117%*
7	**Smoothed error** $\bar{e}_t = 0.2 e_t + (1 - 0.2)\ \bar{e}_{t-1}$	4.6	2.7	16.9	14.2	4.5	–8.6
8	**Mean Absolute Deviation** $MAD_t = 0.2 \lvert e_t \rvert + (1 - 0.2)\ MAD_{t-1}$	12.6	11.1	23.7	19.5	22.4	30.1
9	**Tracking signal** $T_t = \bar{e}_t / MAD_t$	0.4	0.2	0.7	0.7	0.2	–0.3

Mean Squared Error (MSE)	1819
Mean Absolute Percentage Error (MAPE)	37%

Chapter 10

QUESTION 1. For a demand situation where the average demand per week was 300 units and the standard deviation 40 per week and replenishment orders were delayed on average by two weeks, what re-order level would be required to offer a *vendor service level* or probability of not running out of stock per occasion of 96 per cent?

From the Appendix for 96% $u_{0.04} = 1.75$ hence the re-order level M from Equation 10. 1 is defined by:

$$M = \bar{D}L + u_{0.04}\sigma_d\sqrt{L}$$

$$M = 300 \times 2 + 1.75 \times 40\sqrt{2} = 600 + 99$$

$$M = 699 \text{ units}$$

QUESTION 2. For the situation described in Question 1, what *vendor service level* or probability of not running out of stock per occasion would be offered by a re-order level of 720 units?

By transposing Equation 10.1 to define the value of the normal standard variable such that:

$$u_x = (M - \bar{D}L)/\sigma_d\sqrt{L}$$

$$u_x = (720 - 300 \times 2)/40\sqrt{2}$$

$$u_x = (120)/\ 40\sqrt{2} = 2.12$$

Examining Appendix a value of $u_x = 2.12$ falls between $u = 2.00$ offering 97.7 per cent *vendor service level* and $u = 2.25$ offering 98.8 per cent, so a value of approximately 98 per cent can be assumed.

Chapter 11

QUESTION 1. Where the monthly demand is 100 units, and therefore,

A (annual demand) = 12 × 100 = 1200 and also

C_o (the cost of raising an order per occasion) = 30

i (the annual holding interest rate) = 18% (i.e. 0.18); and

C_m (the stocked item's unit value) = 10.00

From Equation 11. 3, The Economic Order Quantity Q_o is given by:

$$Q_o = \sqrt{\frac{2AC_o}{iC_m}} = \sqrt{\frac{2 \times 1200 \times 30}{0.18 \times 10.00}} = 200 \text{ units.}$$

Question 2. The increase in annual operating costs (ordering + storage) which occurs if replenishment orders of higher (or lower) than the EOQ are used is defined by Equation 11.6 such that if the increase in order size x by using a replenishment order of 400 rather than the EOQ of 200 is given by:

$$x = \left(\frac{q}{Q_o} - 1\right) = \left(\frac{400}{200} - 1\right) = 1.0 \text{ or } 100 \text{ per cent,}$$

then from Equation 11.6 the increase in operating costs y is given by:

$$y = \frac{x^2}{2(1 + x)} = \frac{1.0 \times 1.0}{2 \times (1 + 1.0)} = 0.25 \text{ or } 25 \text{ per cent.}$$

The annual operating costs (ordering + replenishment) when operating at the EOQ Q_o of 200 units are given by Equation 11.1 such that (assuming $s = 0$)

$$C_{A_{Q_o}} = \left(\frac{A}{Q_o}\right)C_o + \left(\frac{Q_o}{2}\right)iC_m$$

$$C_{A_{Q_o}} = \left(\frac{1200}{200}\right) \times 30 + \left(\frac{200}{2}\right) \times 0.18 \times 10$$

$$C_{A_{Q_o}} = 180 + 180 = 360.$$

(Note: At the Economic Order Quantity replenishment ordering costs equal storage costs)

The annual operating costs (ordering + replenishment) when operating at a replenishment quantity q of 400 units are given by Equation 11.1 such that:

$$C_{A_q} = \left(\frac{A}{q}\right)C_o + \left(\frac{q}{2}\right)iC_m$$

$$C_{A_q} = \left(\frac{1200}{400}\right) \times 30 + \left(\frac{400}{2}\right) \times 0.18 \times 10$$

$$C_{A_q} = 90 + 360 = 450.$$

The increase in annual operating costs is then confirmed as:

$$y = \frac{(450 - 360)}{360} = 0.25 \text{ or 25 per cent.}$$

QUESTION 3. If replenishment orders of 400 units are used, the minimum discount on purchase price per unit δ_T must be achieved for total annual inventory costs (ordering + storage + purchasing/acquisition) to be no higher than at the EOQ is defined by Equation 11.7, given that the increase in replenishment order size x from above is 1.0 or 100 per cent. It then follows that:

$$\delta_T > \frac{C_o x^2}{(1 + x)(C_o(1 + x) + Q_o C_m)} = \frac{30 \times 1.0 \times 1.0}{(1 + 1.0) \times (30 \times (1 + 1.0) + 200 \times 10.00)}$$

$\delta_T > 0.00728$ or 0.728 per cent giving a minimum bid price per unit of 9.93.

The total annual inventory costs (ordering + storage + purchase/acquisition) when operating at the EOQ Q_o at a unit price C_m of 10.00 is given by:

$$C_{T_{Q_o}} = \left(\frac{A}{Q_o}\right)Co + \left(\frac{Q_o}{2}\right)iC_m + AC_m$$

$$C_{T_{Q_o}} = \left(\frac{1200}{200}\right) \times 30 + \left(\frac{200}{2}\right) \times 0.18 \times 10 + 1200 \times 10$$

$$C_{T_{Q_o}} = 180 + 180 + 12\,000 = 12\,360.$$

The total annual inventory costs (ordering + storage + purchase/acquisition) when operating at the EOQ Q_o at a unit price C_m of 9.58 is given by:

$$C_{A_q} = \left(\frac{A}{q}\right)C_o + \left(\frac{q}{2}\right)iC_m + AC_m$$

$$C_{A_q} = \left(\frac{1200}{400}\right) \times 30 + \left(\frac{400}{2}\right) \times 0.18 \times 9.93 + 1200 \times 9.93$$

$$C_{A_q} = 90 + 357.5 + 11\,916 = 12\,363.5$$

which within the slight inaccuracy caused by rounding errors equals $C_{T_{Q_o}} = 12\,360$.

Chapter 12

QUESTION 1. For the demand and lead-time situation described in Question 1, Chapter 10, what 'vendor service level' and 'customer service level' would be offered when operating at a re-order level of 682 units and a replenishment order size of 1000 units if the average overshoot is assumed to be 25.5 units?

The effective re-order level M' is 682 – 25.5 = 656.5 units. By transposing Equation 10.1 to define the value of the normal standard variable such that:

$$u_x = (M' - \bar{D}L)/\sigma_d\sqrt{L}$$
$$u_x = (656.5 - 300 \times 2)/40\sqrt{2}$$
$$u_x = (56.5)/40\sqrt{2} \approx 1.$$

From the Appendix for $u_x = 1$, $E(u) = 0.083$, which produces a 'vendor service level' of only 84.1 per cent.

However, by substituting in Equation 12.1, the *customer service level* P' is defined as:

$$P' = 1 - \frac{E(u)\sigma_d\sqrt{L}}{q}$$

$$P' = 1 - \frac{0.083 \times 40\sqrt{2}}{1000} = 0.9953.$$

This producing a corresponding 'customer service level' of 99.53 per cent.

Chapter 13

Question 1. For the demand and lead-time situation described in Question 1, Chapter 10, what 'vendor service level' and 'customer service level' would be offered when operating a re-order cycle policy with a maximum stock level *S* of 3800 units and a review period *R* of ten weeks?

Transposing Equation 13.5:

$$u_x = \left(\frac{S - \bar{D}(R + L)}{\sigma_d\sqrt{R + L}}\right)$$

$$u_x = \left(\frac{3800 - 300 \times (10 + 2)}{40\sqrt{10 + 2}}\right) = 1.44.$$

From the Appendix for $u_x = 1.44$ produces a 'vendor service level' of 92.7 per cent.

For $u_x = 1.44$, the corresponding value of $E(u) = 0.033$, so substituting in Equation 13.4 produces:

$$P' = 1 - \frac{E(u)\sigma_d\sqrt{R + L}}{R\bar{D}}$$

$$P' = 1 - \frac{0.033 \times 40\sqrt{10 + 2}}{10 \times 300} = 0.9985$$

or a 'customer service level' of 98.85 per cent.

Index